GHOSTS OF THE BROADS

By Chas. Sampson

Jarrold Publishing, Norwich

ISBN 0-7117-0238-1
© R. D. B. Sutton 1973
Published by Jarrold Publishing, Norwich
Printed in Great Britain. 6/90

Preface

For many years since I was given a copy of the original of this book, I have had a real fascination for it and a wish to find a way to republish.

Apart from this, I was most interested in the author and after a lot of research and the most kind help of the Norwich Central Library, the following facts emerged:

In 1931 Dr Sampson is listed as having three addresses: 48 Harley Street, London W1; 76 Beulah Hill, London SE19; and The Terrace House, 13 Camberwell Green, London. Dr Sampson appears in the *Medical Directory* and *Medical Register* until 1940 and so he presumably died around this year. In these directories there are listed a very large number of appointments and qualifications held by Dr Sampson, the most important being *Licentiate of Society of Apothecaries*, London 1905, and *Licentiate in Medicine and Surgery of the Society of Apothecaries*, London 1909. Dr Sampson published some medical works which are mentioned in the *Medical Directory*; the titles given are: *Subconscious Activities* (no date given), *Cérébration Retardée*, Paris 1925, and *New Treatment for Rheumatism and Allied Disorders*, Aix-les-Bains 1934.

Last year with the most generous help of Mr Foxlow of Foxlow Publications Ltd, 19 Harcourt Street, Marylebone, I was able to obtain the copyright and present to you this new edition with its original text, but with the addition of photographs for whose help I am indebted to Judy Brooks of Fundenhall and Peter Lange of Harleston for their imagination and skill. Also, I would like to thank Jarrold Publishing without whose real help and encouragement this book would not again be in print.

Finally, to so many others who have given advice, been photographed and helped in every way, I do give most grateful thanks. A final tribute to Dr Charles Sampson for writing a book on ghosts that so many people can enjoy.

Richard Sutton
Pulham Market

Author's Introduction

In placing this little book in the hands of the reader, the author wishes to thank all those who have assisted in its compilation, and hopes that its perusal will charm those who scan its pages as much as it rejoiced the writer's heart in 'getting together' the material within its covers. This has been no mean task, entailing searches and researches to an almost incredible extent. Many of the items are historically accurate, whilst a good deal has, of necessity, had to be gleaned from traditions and unwritten records direct from the lips of the local indigenes. How much of it is actually true must be left to the gentle reader's own discretion, but it makes interesting and entertaining reading, especially to all those who are familiar with the places mentioned. All the world loves a lover, and most of us love a good succulent ghost-story. Here we have stories of both.

As is well-known, the periodicity of apparitions comes around with extraordinary accuracy, definite manifestations occurring on certain days, such as St Mark's Day, 5 March, St Anthony's Day, 13 June, and All Hallows E'en, 31 October. Many of these appearances and happenings are specially interesting in the fact that, although the calendar has suffered many changes since their first inception, they have accommodated themselves to the new order without changing their date. Again, I would ask the reader to allow me to remind him that all apparitions are not perceptible to everybody. Some psychically sensitive people can see them, but not necessarily all of them. This is due to the fact that certain perceptions can only 'tune-in', as in 'wireless', to certain wave-lengths or vibrations, just as only certain ears are capable of hearing certain sounds, whilst others suffering from note deafness are incapable of receiving the vibrations of particular notes. No one in these days of enlightenment would dream of saying that spirits or ghosts do not exist, simply because they individually are incapable of seeing them. Think of the enormous number of light-rays which are invisible to the naked eye, yet can be photographically recorded, such, for instance, as the X-rays and the Gamma rays of radium, also the infra-red and the ultra-violet rays, all of which are quite invisible normally. Then there are the light or radio-active emanations from the human body itself, which are known to form what is called the 'aura', so beloved by old-fashioned necromancers till science knocked their bottom out by proving the actual existence of these rays, and that they could be made visible to anybody by the double cyanide screen. (Kilner.) The seers' eyes were susceptible to these rays and their perception was therefore easy to them.

Within the limited compass of these pages it has been impossible to include all the data collected during a period of twenty-five years, but the more important have been chosen for your delectation, and the author prays your acceptance in the same good faith with which these chronicles are offered for the first time in collected form.

Contents

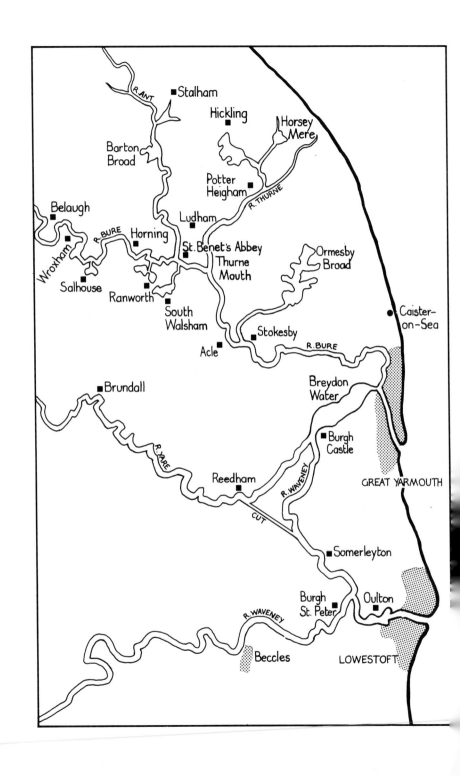

Wroxham

A brilliant and warm sunny afternoon 'neath a blazing sky in mid-July, one of those sweltering days that Norfolk knows so well, scarcely a zephyr anywhere, the trees around the mere are motionless, even the tallest twigs are still, the reeds that line the edge of the water are undisturbed except for an occasional crested grebe who ploughs his way out of them to disappear and reappear at odd intervals in the depths of that limpid lake. The cows at the far end are standing in the water to cool their legs, whilst the dronings of clusters of myriads of gnats is the only sound that breaks the gentle quiet of that peaceful solitude.

It was on just such an afternoon as this on 21 July 1829, that Lord Percival Durand described in his letters to his father the remarkable occurrence which is here related. He was in his yacht, the *Amarylis*, at the time, which was anchored in the River Bure, about two hundred yards from what is today the eastern entrance. He and some friends had gone ashore and were seated beneath the trees looking across the lake, when an old man, very shrivelled and worn, came up to them, leaning on a tall stick, and asked for alms.

'My dear parent', he writes, '. . . He was an uncanny looking person, whom one might reasonably expect to live in a hole in the ground, and who could appear and disappear at will. His left eye was gone and sunken into the orbit and closed. The right eye was fixed and looked perpetually downwards and inwards. A forbidding looking person indeed. His mouth was very large, and the lower jaw had dropped somewhat, revealing some ragged and discoloured teeth, several of which were missing. No one saw him arrive, and no one saw exactly what eventually became of him when he left us.

' "Who are you?" we asked, thinking that it might prove interesting to draw him into conversation and so learn something of this beautiful inland sea, which is over a mile long and 120 acres in extent.

' "My name would not interest you, gentlemen, and I have come to warn you that you are trespassing on crown land." His voice I would say was cultured in tone, but there was something about his diction that was not quite English. We were surprised to learn that

we had no right to be here, believing that all this property was held by some private landowner.

' "To whom does it belong?" we enquired.

' "To the crown," he replied, and added emphatically, "To Caesar."

' "To Caesar? What Caesar, pray?"

' "To His Majesty the Emperor Marcus Aurelius Carausius of the Western Empire."

'That the poor fellow was somewhat unbalanced there could now be no doubt, and, appearing quite harmless, we pressed him further.

' "But you have not told us yet who you are, my friend?" I said.

' "I am the Custos Rotulorum for the whole of this part of Britain, and my name is Flavius Mantus."

' "But tell us, Flavius, why are you here today? The Roman Empire relinquished these islands fifteen hundred years ago."

' "You are right, and you are wrong. The 20th Legion of Auxiliaries of the Belgae left here as you say, but the Roman Empire in the West never relinquished these islands. The Empire continues here today as of old, and I am still the Custos here."

' "You are very old then?"

' "Yes, I get older every year. Have you come to see the celebrations?"

' "No, what celebrations?"

' "It is our noble Emperor's birthday today, and in the Stadium here (pointing to the lake) a great festa will take place."

'We looked hard at the waters of this placid Broad and tried to appear interested, but he divined what was passing in our minds, and pointing again to the far corner of the mere with his long stick, said:

' "Do you see the great Caesar's banner floating over the royal box?" We looked and then, our eyes returning to the strange old fellow, we saw that the old man was here no longer, but had changed into a gorgeously uniformed Roman officer. The waters of the Broad had rolled back and transformed themselves into a huge stone wall enclosing a most sumptuous Roman amphitheatre with terraced seats all around, and thousands of silken banners and bannerets were fluttering in the breeze from the copings. The arena was turfed with a velvet sward of surpassing beauty, and thousands of people in Roman costume were flocking from all directions and passing in to their seats. Already there were bands of soldiers in Roman armour strolling about, and several chariots with prancing white chargers were moving around to the far side of this huge hippodrome. We rubbed our eyes and pinched ourselves to try and convince ourselves that we were not dreaming, but it was all genuine enough, and

3

everybody was in happy mood and the noise of this excited concourse floated up towards us.

' "Today," continued this official, "our great Emperor arrives by road from Branudonum, on his return with his fleet from Gessoriacum, and here he comes!" A mighty volume of shouts went up from the amphitheatre, everybody was standing, and a band of trumpets blared their fanfares of rejoicing. A long procession of soldiers began to enter the arena, and presently the place seemed full of cohorts and legions, and then a mighty roar of welcome went up, as a large golden chariot drawn by ten white horses in sumptuous harness came in. Around the chariot were twelve full-grown lions led on golden chains by warriors in gilt armour carrying glistening halberds. The cavalcade made a complete detour of the arena whilst the golden chariot bearing the Roman general took up its position in the centre.

' "See!" exclaimed the Custos, swelling with pride. "There is the greatest man this country has ever known. There stands before you the great General Marcus Aurelius Valerius Carausius, Count of the Saxon Shore, Primicerius Notariorum, Emperor of the Most Noble and Honorable Roman Empire in the West. From Branudonum in the East to Portus Adurni in the South, from Isca in the South-West to Camelon in the North his name is the greatest in all Britannia. See, now he descends from his chariot and leads the way to the royal box. Today is the celebration of his great victory over the raiders from the shores far over the Eastern seas. There come the prisoners he has taken. See them filing in and being arranged in the centre of the arena. They are some of the Danes and Jutes who came in their long ships to attack this peaceful land. Those are the survivors. It was a mighty battle, so I hear. Three hundred and seven triremes put out from these shores to meet the combined forces of a huge enemy fleet. Now look, they kneel before the Emperor and ask for clemency. Lots will be drawn presently to decide who amongst them shall fight the Roman champion."

'Then slowly the entire apparition faded out from our view, dear parent, and in a moment the span of water resumed its normal appearance, and the Roman officer had changed back to the old man once more, and, wandering away amidst the trees, disappeared.'

This strange psychic phenomenon has also been witnessed by several people at odd intervals. Sometimes it occurs towards the end of March, and in the *Gentlemen's Gazette* of 16 April 1709, we find it recorded by an ecclesiastic, one Reverend Thomas Josiah Penston, on a visit from Durham, who states that, 'we were holding a picknick on the banks of a beautiful lake in Norfolke about eleven miles from the ancient city of Norwich when we were suddenly and

4

very peremptorily ordered away by a very undesirable looking person whose appearance and clothes belied his refinements of natural good breeding. As we were somewhat enangered by this unpleasant person's persistence, we made to go away, when suddenly we had to quickly stand aside to make passage for a long procession of regal splendour, the outstanding characters of which were a golden chariot containing a hideous looking man dressed as a Roman general, and drawn by ten white prancing stallions, about a dozen lions led in chains by stalwart Roman soldiers, a band of trumpeters making a great noise, and another band of drummers, followed by several hundreds of long-haired, partly armoured sea-faring men, or sea-soldiers, all chained together. They passed quite close to us, but no one apparently saw us. There must have been seven or eight hundred horsemen in this long procession of archers, pikemen and balista machines. Whither they went or from whence they came I know not, yet they vanished at the lake side. The noise of their passinge was very loud and unmistakable.'

In the *Archives of the North-folk* for 1603, one Benjamin Curtiss, writing of a bathe he had in the Great Broad of Wroxham, near unto Hoveton St John, states:

'Two friends and myself were swiminge across the lake from the Bure-side to that opposite, when strangely enough we felt our feete touche the bottom. Now at this parte there is much water, as much as twelve, and in other places some fourteen feete. We keppe together and presently found ourselves standynge in the middle of a large arena with much seates one above the other all around us. The water was gone and we were standynge there dressed as Roman officers. What is more astonishing still, we were not surprysed neither were we incommoded by this piece of enchantment, but rather were we quite accustomed to it, so that we forgette that we had been batheinge. The top of the amphitheatre was all opened to the skye, and many flagges of divers colors floated in the wyndes from the top of the walles.'

Friend Curtiss then continues a long and tiring description of what took place, the people coming into their seats, the arrival of a huge procession of regal grandeur 'many myles longe', and the blowing of a large concourse of trumpets, and a band of several hundreds of men, 'all cheynied together'. It was all over in a few minutes, and evidently they continued their swim.

On arriving at the bank, they partook of some food, and then decided to find out if they had all seen or experienced the same episode. They suggested that they should each 'telle a storey', and Curtiss told what he had seen. His friends repeated the narrative, and they knew that each had seen the same terrifying apparition'.

In Calvert's *Legend of the Lake*, published in 1741, we again find reference to the psychic manifestations of the Broad:

> While through the trees of yonder lake,
> There comes a cavalcade of horsemen near.
> Gaze not upon these Romans, friends,
> For fear their eyes may meet with thine.
> Stand back, well back, and let them pass,
> These denizens of death and close thine orbs,
> Lest out upon a scene of death they fall,
> In hapless misery for those who play
> Their parts, for nigh a thousand years.
> Doomed for a term to re-enact
> The life they led, the parts they played;
> Go not with them, look not at them, but
> Pray for them, dear friend, for they
> Are dead.

And so runs the story of Wroxham Broad. Many a time have I lingered on its banks on the off-chance of meeting a disreputable looking old man, who might any moment change into a Roman officer.

Only once I saw a being who might have satisfied my quest and yearning, but he worked at the farm, and in reality was an extraordinarily good fellow, and once did me a very good service, but there was nothing of the Custos Rotulorum about him.

This apparition is said to occur several times between the Ides of March and the Nones of October, notably on the 13 and 16 April, 7 and 21 May, 1, 4 and 11 June, only once in July, and then on 5, 13 and 19 of August, on 15, 13, 22 and 26 September, and on 7 and 9 October.

It will be noticed that invariably the first performance in each month takes place on the nones of that month, the nones, according to the Roman Calendar, falling on the fifth day of each month except in March, May, July and October, when they fall on the seventh day. On any of these occasions it is quite easy from the banks or in a boat to hear the cheering as of a vast multitude in the distance coming from the middle of those placid waters if you are only the least bit psychically sensitive.

The local residents keep a very discreet silence on these phenomena, and quite reasonably too, for the Broad is so beautiful and peaceful, they do not want its serenity interfered with.

According to *Day's Chronicles of East Anglia*, 1825, the royal progress of Carausius, the founder of the Royal Mint in London, complete with lions and prisoners comes down what is still the village street in Wroxham on its way from Brancaster, the Roman fortress and citadel which defended the Wash.

Oulton

Ever seen the Ghost Wherry? The great white ship with white sails that visits Oulton Broad every year? Well, listen, and I'll tell you the story.

Back in 1851, on a dark September evening, a huge wherry specially built for carrying cargo into the inland waters of Norfolk and Suffolk, made a historic voyage that will go down to posterity. She was named the *Mayfly*, and although this insect after which she was called has only a brief span of life of one day, in its existence, yet this vessel belies her name and still lives, and apparently will continue to do so until the end of time.

The *Mayfly*, a large vessel of English oak and teak, was captained by a man called Stevenson, a chap with a quick tongue, a quicker temper, and, quickest of all, fists like legs of mutton. He was a man of about forty-five with reddish hair, and a taste for ale, a gammy leg, and an eye which could see further than most men's. He had served fifteen years before the mast, sailed the Seven Seas, and rounded the Horn in all weathers heaps of times. His temper was his undoing, and once when in Rangoon he fought five men single-handed in the fo'c'stle. They punished him badly, but he was proof against fists and heavy boots, and two men fell to his straight left and never recovered. One had his face smashed in, whilst the other two had several ribs stove in, and fractured collar-bones. 'Blood' Stevenson was a bruiser of the first order and had he been properly trained for the ring, might have made a fortune as England's 'white hope', but he wasn't, and so he remained a dangerous man to deal with, and one whose name was dreaded even by those who had only heard of and never met him. He did a three years' stretch for the affair in Rangoon, and then got a job as mate on a Yankee hot-ship. After battering and hammering a Swede off the coast of Florida, he deemed it wise to get another ship as soon as possible back to England. After two months of idleness at home he ran across the firm who owned the *Mayfly*, and although he never had his ticket, he acted as master, and took command of this vessel. At the request of Stevenson, who had never used a tiller-steered vessel before, a wheel was installed, which made the ship look more like a barge than a wherry, whilst he brought along a ship's compass of his own, in order that he might feel more at home when navigating, even though he would never have occasion to use it in those narrow waterways. She was a fine craft, with plenty of canvas, could lick the other wherries hands down at her trade, and worked between Yarmouth and Beccles. It was said she did the fifteen-mile trip quicker than any other vessel in those parts, due of course to her spread of canvas and the men who worked her.

One day, about four years after 'Blood' Stevenson took over, the owners called him into their office at Beccles and said:

'Captain Stevenson, we want to send a large chest of money to the bank at Yarmouth, and feel that it would be safer by water than road, in view of the fact that there are possibilities which give us good reason to believe that it would never reach there, if taken by land.'

'Is it a large amount, gentlemen?' he enquired.

'Well, it is rather,' they replied, 'somewhere in the region of four hundred thousand pounds.'

'It certainly never would get to Yarmouth by road,' he answered, the directors not quite following his train of thought.

'It has been suggested that we send it by water on the *Mayfly*, and in order to disarm any suspicion it is further suggested that Miss Millicent, the daughter of Mr Dormey here, goes with you. The chest can outwardly be hers, and a lady's trunk on board with the lady herself would never raise the slightest question.'

'An excellent idea, gentlemen,' said 'Blood', and the vision of this beautiful and lovely young girl aboard his ship in his care sent his blood dancing through his arteries. It was accordingly arranged that Miss Millicent should go and stay with an imaginary aunt at Yarmouth, and take enough clothes to last a month or six weeks.

Now, Miss Millicent had often come aboard at Beccles and chatted with the skipper, and the skipper, being very human, had formed an attachment to this young and desirable girl, which rather flattered her childish vanity, and though he was old enough twice over to be her father, yet she saw in him an adorable Hercules, but had the good sense of discretion and never let him know it. His appearance she gave nought for, and like all women, where she loved, looks counted for nothing.

'Blood' had a mate called 'Jack'. No one ever heard his other name, and he was always known as plain 'Jack' to everybody. Now this mate was also very much in love with Miss Millicent, but dared not declare it for fear of losing his job instantly, and it is very doubtful whether she had ever so much as favoured him with a passing glance. He was just a simple, ordinary wherry-man, in her father's employ,

and it merely began and ended there. Jack was somewhat religiously inclined, and 'attended' regularly when he could, and no one ever heard a foul word slip from him in all the years he had faithfully served his employer.

There was another man, and a boy, whom 'Blood' had signed on, the man having sailed with him on many occasions in years gone by, and was of much the same kidney as the skipper, if not quite so ungoodly to look upon, whilst the boy, a sturdy young sapling of seventeen named Bert Entwistle, acted as cook, deckie, stevedore, sail-hand, errand boy and drudge, did practically the entire work of the ship, and that without a murmur.

Now it was so arranged that on the night of the transfer of this money to Yarmouth, a large chest containing two armed men should be sent by road, as a trap for anyone who might be abroad by night and waylay the cart. The driver and boy were also prepared for any contingency.

It was about 10 p.m. when the cart departed, and half-an-hour later the owner's daughter came aboard, her 'box' having come down earlier in the evening and been stowed. 'Daddy' came down to the quay with her, and having given her some final greetings and messages for her auntie in Great Yarmouth, kissed her, and saw the *Mayfly* off. Little did he realise that that would be the last he would see of his beautiful daughter, the *Mayfly*, or the money.

The cart arrived at Yarmouth without the slightest molestation and two very cramped men crawled out of the box at the end of their journey, which had been to no purpose.

The *Mayfly*, on the other hand, put down stream and ploughed her way along the tortuous windings of the Waveney until passing Burgh St. Peters, she ran out into Oulton Dyke and made up past Somerleyton and St Olaves. On reaching Breydon Water, just where Burgh Castle looms up on the right, the captain called the mate to him and said:

'Jack, are you going to throw in your lot with us, or be thrown overboard?' The mate gasped, and terror seized him as in a flash he realised what was in the wind.

'What – what do you mean, skipper?' he enquired, quaking from head to foot.

'Mean? Never mind what I mean. This ship is mine, and everything that's in it. Clear?'

'But you're not going to steal the ship?' asked the mate terrified at the boldness of the man.

'I'm not a thief, if that's what you're trying to call me. I'm just making myself a handsome present, that's all. Clear?'

'But, Captain, what about Miss Millicent?'

'Oh, Hell to you, you white-livered, psalm-singing heretic. I give you three minutes to leave the ship.'

'But do you expect me to——'

He never finished the sentence. With a shout the skipper sprang on him. There was a terrific struggle, the moon came out from behind a cloud, there was a heavy splash, and 'Blood' Stevenson returned to the wheel.

The big sail was full, the mast was creaking at the strain, and the water was running away from the bow at about seven knots. It was a wonderful night now the moon was up, and Breydon was soon left behind. Down the Yare sped the wherry, every ounce of canvas doing its duty. The town of Yarmouth was asleep, and but for an occasional street-lamp on the jetties throwing its reflection on the ebbing waters of the river, the place was wrapped in slumber. Out past the little village of Gorleston and into the open sea the *Mayfly* sped along as she had never done before. The captain was determined to have a good start in case of pursuit, and a stiff blow from the nor'-west favoured his plans.

It wasn't long before the girl below became aware of the unusual motion of the ship, came on deck to see where they were, and was just in time to see the last flickering of the lights on shore disappearing as their distance from it increased.

On seeing her come up, Stevenson called to the other man, and said:

'Take the wheel George, and keep her dead on her present bearing. I'll relieve you later.' Then going up to the girl, he said:

'Miss Millicent, we are at sea.'

'Yes', she replied, somewhat taken aback.

'I thought it would be a good idea to have a cruise and try the old bird out on the briny.'

'But she's not built for it, is she?' she replied, feeling she knew enough to tell him that wherries were not intended for sea-going purposes.

'Trust me, lady. I could sail this ship to Jericho and back. Your Pa said before we left, "Don't hurry to get to Yarmouth. Any time'll do." So here we are.'

'Oh, isn't it wonderful,' she replied, 'we *are* moving!'

'Moving? My dear girl!' – she was pleased; it was the first time he had ever called her that – 'This is nothing. You wait till we alter the course, and she begins to heel over to it. We'll show 'em how we can mop along. Now you slip back to bed and I'll send some tea to you in the morning.'

She did as she was bid, went below and turned in, but not without a parting glance at 'Blood', and a coy little twinkle in her left eye.

By the following morning they were nearer the Dutch coast than the English, and speeding south before a full and happy wind. The young girl was a little sick, and the boy Bert very sorry for himself, but the two arch-villains at the tiller of destiny never turned a hair. Down the Channel they went, and out on to the heaving bosom of the broad Atlantic. On the second day out the lady passenger became a little desirous of getting home, and mentioned it to the skipper.

'Home, Missie? Home? What d'you want to go home for? Aren't you happy on board here? Lookee here, now. I've a proposition to make to you. You're not a bad little wench, and I'd feel the proudest man in the world if you'd marry me.'

She gasped and was very surprised that this man who had never spoken a word of love to her, but for whom she nursed a deep admiration, should have spoken of matrimony to her without any preamble or even the slightest expression of affection.

'Oh, Mr er – Captain, I must think this over. We don't know each other very well yet, do we?' she replied, with a coaxing tone of possibility in her negation.

'Oh, that don't matter a damn – er (he saw her wince) – I beg your pardon, Miss, but don't let that come 'tween you and your sleep.'

'But I don't understand you, Captain. You see, I must have time to consider it, and ask my Papa. And then, if he says I may, then – well————'

'Papa! Papa, indeed! We don't want none of the papa business here.' She was beginning to feel a little frightened. 'Well, you see, Missie, it's like this. As long as you're on my ship you have to fall in with what I say, always. That is the law of the sea. Whatever the captain says, goes. Clear? Very well, then, you may as well make up your mind to like me, seeing that you're going to live with me; besides it'd look better all the way round. This is my ship and everything aboard, including yourself, so put a good face on it, sweetheart, and fall in with things as you find 'em.'

Did she hear aright? Were her ears playing her false? There was this great violent bull of a man telling her all this, and not a word of love. She was mistaken in him. All her calculations of him were wrecked. The ship and everything on it was his. Her father hadn't told her anything of this. She was a little alarmed. How could it be his? And the money? That certainly couldn't either.

'I don't understand you quite, Captain. Did you say the ship was yours?'

'I did.'

'Ah, yes, you sailors always speak like that of your command; isn't that so? She isn't really your property, your very own. How shall I put it. Well, you're not the owner?'

'I *am* the owner. Sixty-four sixty-fourths of this ship is mine. The whole lot of her. Mine to do what I like with. And everything on board as well, including yourself.'

'When are we going back to Yarmouth?'

'Never!' He had shot his bolt, and it went straight on the mark. The girl stiffened and drew back.

'Never?' she gasped, with a frightened tremor in her voice.

'No, we shall never make Yarmouth or Beccles again. We've seen the last of the old country this side of the grave, so you'd better chuck in your lot with mine, and be a help instead of a hindrance.'

'Do you mean to say you're stealing the ship? And all the money?' she asked, her little face deathly pale, and her eyes dark and large, blazing with fear.

'Now, lookee here, Missie, it's no use us having any bandy of words about all this. What I've told you is true. From the moment we left Beccles, this ship, the money, you, and everything on this ship belonged to me. Clear? Very good, then. I am going to take you for my wedded wife now, with no more questions or arguments about it. Clear? We'll discuss our plans later. Come down to the cabin, now.'

The girl uttered a cry and tried hard to keep her nerve, but he took her by the arm and led her to the companion at the head of the stairs she stopped and faced him.

'Captain Stevenson,' she said, in a defensive, imperious tone, 'what do you think you——' She didn't finish the sentence. His strong arm just simply lifted her off her feet, and carried her below. A moment later there was a loud scream, a piteous cry, and the sound of sobbing reached the man at the wheel, but he grimly stared out across the waste of waters, his hands gripping the wheel perhaps a little tighter, and his jaw well set.

When 'Blood' came on deck he was very angry, red of face, and had evidently been drinking. He pushed the helmsman away from the wheel and took it himself.

That night the boy Bert was doing his 'trick' at the wheel, when from below there came up the most ghastly screams imaginable and presently the girl suddenly appeared on deck in her nightdress, pursued by the drunken skipper. She was bleeding from a gash in her neck, and the captain's face, hands and clothes were covered with blood.

The man whom Bert had relieved came up on deck and tried to stop the rush of the captain, and they closed. The fight was a fearful affair. These two men, both powerful and fearless, wrestled with each other all over the deck. The captain's hands tried to get his throat and the sailor's knee was in his stomach, and his hand was up under his assailant's chin forcing his head backwards. They stumbled and fell over each other time after time in a vain effort to master each other, when suddenly the captain made a feint, let go his man, swung his big fist clean into his face, and as he fell, seized his unconscious victim and flung him into the sea. The boy at the helm left the wheel, raced forward to save the girl from the captain's fury, and was just in time to see him fall dead at her feet with a knife thrust clean through his heart. Where she had found the weapon no one will ever know, but she aimed at him the blow that saved her from the storm of his uncontrollable rage. As Bert came to help her, she uttered a piercing scream of anguish, flung her arms above her head, and her dead body fell across the corpse of her persecutor.

The boy was staggered. Alone on a stolen ship, with two dead people lying on the deck before him, his position was a piteous one indeed. To sail the vessel home was beyond him, for he could neither read nor write, and as for navigating he had not the faintest knowledge of a compass, and as for reading a chart he was hopelessly beaten. As a deckie and a cook he found no difficulty, but when it came to understanding winds, and steering a course, he was in very truth completely 'at sea', and in every sense of the word, too. His only chance of escape was to wait for daylight, so he lashed the wheel, let the *Mayfly* run free, and went below and cooked himself a huge meal.

The following morning he awoke from a deep alcoholic sleep and went on deck. The two bodies still lay where they had been all night, so he set about getting the dinghy over the side and lashing it so that he might cut her free and say good-bye to the ship. Into the dinghy he packed quantities of foodstuff, a water-beaker, some warm rugs, several bottles of rum, a cork-screw, and a gun with some cartridges. Then, packing his own bundle of belongings, he stepped into the waiting boat, stepped the mast, set the sails, and took with him a large Union Jack on a staff.

With a slash of his knife, the *Mayfly* raced away with her awful consignment, and Bert was soon left behind in his little craft on the surging billows of the open main. A mist soon hid the abandoned vessel from view, and Bert found himself out upon the vast waste of waters alone. But he was not afraid. That night he prayed for help, and he saw a faint white light coming towards him. It was a ship. His prayer had been answered. As she came closer he tried to signal her by striking matches, but presently there was a rushing, mighty wind, and a huge white ship with one mast and one large mainsail and white decks and sides came by. She was covered all over with phosphorescence, and as she went by he could see all her lines glistening with this eerie light. Suddenly a girl in white, pursued by a man all in white, raced around the deck screaming, and at last they fell in a heap near the wheel. The wash from the vessel as she passed rocked his dinghy, and he caught her name as she sped by. It was the *Mayfly*, which had started on her death cruise, from which she was destined never to make port. She had left behind a choking, foul smell of something burning which irritated his throat and stung his eyes unmercifully. Except for the weird creaking of her mast and sail, she made no sound, and sped away in a phosphorescent glow on her wild and abandoned course. Then he fainted. When he came to, he was in a clean little white bed, with two men standing by his side.

'Yes,' said one, 'that'll bring him round.'

He was very ill for a long time, and was later transferred to a hospital ashore. His whereabouts were a mystery to him, and he had sufficient sense to fear that if he made any enquiries he might be regarded as mental, which he most certainly was not, although he had been through enough to unbalance a stronger mind than his. Just before his discharge from the Devon and Cornwall General Hospital at Plymouth, he sent to the owner of the *Mayfly* at Beccles, who went down and brought him home, and listened to the story of his horrifying experience.

'And may you well never see 'er again, 'bor,' he told his employer. 'She's a death-ship and has joined the hell-fleet. A man was telling me in 'orspital that knew all about 'em, an' 'e said: "Bert, when a ship is stolen and there's murder on board, she joins the devil's navy, and never makes port. She sails till the trumpet calls her. And where-ever she goes, she leaves death in her wake." Don't look for 'er, sir. Don't look for 'er, or something'll befall you.'

One night the owner was fishing with Bert on Oulton Broad from a moored dinghy with a dimmed lamp in the boat, when suddenly the air became heavy like a sponge full of treacle. It had been drizzling. The whole atmosphere became so oppressive it was difficult to breathe. A strong, heavy, acrid smell of something burning caught the nostrils and the throat, nearly strangling in its intensity. He looked up and to his horror he saw the *Mayfly* coming down from the direction of the Dyke, heeling over to no wind at all, yet with her sails full. Her masts and sails, lines, deck, seams and planking were all outlined in phosphorescence, her mainsail glowing all over and yet translucent, and she was putting up a huge bow-wave as she raced wildly along. A skeleton was at the wheel and as she rushed past, he heard his daughter scream at the top of her voice, 'Father, save me'. And then he saw her pursued by the villain 'Blood' and finally fall dead, just as it had all happened three years before. Round the Broad the wherry tore at a terrifying pace, never halting, easing up, or tacking, but just racing along impelled by some irresistible internal force. Behind her she left a sulphurous, sickening smell, and a semi-luminous wake, and in a minute or two she was out of the Broad again and heading up the Dyke.

' 'Bor,' said Bert, in a voice saddened and thickened with emotion, 'it's the 24th June. Three years ago today was the fatal day', and looking round, he saw his master lying dead in the bottom of the boat.

And so it goes on. Every year on 24 June, about 12.30 a.m. the *Mayfly* comes to Oulton Broad, trying to make her home port, but never succeeding.

With the Stygian ensign fluttering at her main, and ploughing her way through the mass of boats and light craft moored at the village end – you can actually see her passing right through them and leaving them undamaged – she careers madly along on her never-ending journey.

Those who have seen her have always heard of a death soon after. The British Psychical Phenomena Association have investigated it, and their findings are recorded in their transactions, Vol. 98, pages 127–172, and 401, 406, and 863. The International Society of Metaphysics has tried for the last seven years to make records of this chthonic manifestation by means of the selenic cell and the thermionic valve. They are building a special high-speed film camera to try and get her this year, whilst Professor Erst, of Munich, and Dr Paolo Sevrini, from Rome, are coming specially to investigate it. An attempt this year is to be made to photograph her, and four distinct societies are going to have a shot at it.

Two daily papers are interesting themselves quietly in the proposal, and we will see if anything like success attends their efforts.

And that is the story, which you will never hear from the local people, because they do not like it, which is only reasonable after all.

Personally, I wouldn't be on Oulton Broad on the night of June the 24th for anything in the world. I have no desire to see this ghost-wherry, this ship of Hell, with bloody murder on her deck and Death at the helm.

Thurne Mouth

It was in 1926 I first heard the story of the ghost of Thurne Mouth. You are quite sure, dear reader, you know the place I refer to? To make it quite certain, let us place it. Coming up the Bure from Acle you arrive at the junction of the Thurne with the Bure, the Bure winding away to the left towards Horning and Wroxham, and the Thurne to the right in the direction of Potter Heigham. Well, the identical spot where I heard this story is just this side of that junction on the starboard hand, about thirty yards down, say midway between the effluent of the Thurne and the little Dyke that runs up to Boundary House, and where you can get eggs, milk and cream second to none in the kingdom.

It was a glorious afternoon in July – the 15th, to be correct – not a fleck in the sky and a broiling sun just licking down on a boat-load of would-be yachtsmen, straight up from the sea (perhaps). George was cleaning up the galley in preparation for the next occasion, after which it would need doing all over again; Don was trying to write to a girl he had met at Norwich at a cinema there – a brunette for a cert, but he is not giving anything away – and killing flies at the same time. I can see him now, with puzzled brow, a pen in one hand and a fly swatter in the other. Then there was Steve, a good fellow forsooth, inclined to be a little shy, but a hell-of-a-feller on deck with a broom. He was fishing. No, please don't ask me what for. I don't believe he knew himself. And, finally, myself.

We had berthed our little yacht alongside a most excellent camp-sheathing provided by a generous land-owner, and for want of something better to do, I called over a cowman who had come down to the meadow for the cows, to engage him in conversation, and possibly learn something about the place. That's the worst of having an enquiring turn of mind, but if I hadn't, well, these chronicles would never have come into existence.

Anyway, he came, or rather shambled, over, and agreed with me it was a splendid day and that the weather was, perhaps yes, a trifle otter'n yesterday. He was a tall, heavily-built man, perhaps a little bent with advancing years, and wore brownish clothes, leggings and heavy boots. His stick with which he walked was a crooked ash, and he held an empty clay between his teeth. His expression was of the rigid and set type common to agricultural workers, and his eyes, small and beady, held a sinister gleam. His hat was a soft felt that had lost its shape many years ago. It is all so fresh in my mind, it might have happened today.

'Do I know anything about the folks round about 'ere, did you say, 'Bor?' he asked, and then continued by answering his own question in true North-folk style. "'Ess, I knows more'n I'd care to tell, leastways. Ghosts? Oh, ah! There be a ghost 'ere all right, too; at least they do say as there's one what 'angs round 'bout 'ere occasional.'

He did not need much goading, for he was evidently very chattily inclined, so he knocked out his empty pipe as a hint, and said:

"'Ess, aw'll tell'ee.'

I will now give you the story as he gave it to me, except for the vernacular, which would make it laborious reading if you are not familiar with the local dialect, and secondly, my knowledge of it is so scanty I should spoil the story. So you will accept it, I pray, in good, simple, homely English instead.

Once upon a time, many, many years ago – say about eighty or ninety – there lived a beautiful girl in that house over yonder, still called the Sunny-Side house. Well, her name was Phyllis, and a lovelier young creature it would be hard to find. She had long warm brown ringlets that fell about her neck and shoulders like a garland of flowers. And she was as good as she was beautiful. Everywhere she went she was dearly loved by all who met her, and her love for her home was a devotion beyond all words. Her father, the bailiff for this estate, and her mother, she just worshipped, and her elder sister Betsy and her little brother James she just doted upon. And that must have meant a good deal, for she was so lovely that to be loved by her was more than wonderful. But little Phyllis loved everybody. All the little schoolchildren in the village used to run after her, for the mere sake of her smile, her pretty voice, and even to be near her.

From an infant she had been brought up to respect her parents' wishes before anything else in the world, even her own interests, and so, when she reached the age at which youth begins to look about a bit, she found she was already enamoured of one of her father's ploughmen, a young fellow of estimable mien and good character, but nevertheless a workman, whilst her father had actually encouraged a young man by the name of Bert Isaac. (Isaac is not as one might suppose, a Hebrew surname in Norfolk, although the same name with a final 's' invariably is so, the world over. I should imagine, nevertheless, that the surname of Isaac is of Semetic origin, probably emanating from Holland a couple of centuries back, when Dutch refugees almost colonised the littorals of Norfolk, Suffolk and Essex).

Now young Isaac was but a lad, a mere boy of twenty-two or three, and not old enough to think of taking to himself a wife, and as for Phyllis, she was only a slip of a youngster still, and at eighteen and a country maid at that, was scarcely ready to take her place in the world of matrimony. Nevertheless, her father sternly resented any representations on the farmhand's behalf, and threatened that if there was going to be any nonsense in that direction, William Ethelwistle would have to go; all of which was decidedly unfair and ungenerous, seeing that although William was, after all, only a labouring man, yet when Phyllis's father had been stricken down with pneumonia on two occasions it was William Ethelwistle who did his master's job and his own as well; in fact, he ran the entire farm, and marketed the produce with as equal success as attended the invalid at his best, and one point more in his favour, he did not drink. It is a sad reflection on the master, but nevertheless true, that during his temporary supervision of the farm there was a distinct jump in the profits, and the financial return clearly showed that even if he could neither read nor write, he could barter and sell, and his eye was as keenly capable of appreciating the value of money as anyone else's.

Well, it so happened that one day the father of the girl was taken ill, very ill, and was 'laid by' for over a year, and during this time Bert had been asked to look after the farm interests because William had been sent away on account of the girl losing her head more than ever over him. But what a mess this young boy made of things! In fact, you may scarcely credit it, but he made such a jumble of everything that hands, who could ill be spared, left, accounts went all wrong, and things came to such a pass that the farmer and his wife were only too glad to send for William Ethelwistle and beg him to come back. He did so.

By this time Phyllis had grown into young womanhood and William had learned to read and write and do sums. He had developed into a steady young man who could take his place with all the Berts who cared to show up, and there were plenty, you can take it from me, because the attraction at the farm tended to increase rather than otherwise, and Phyllis liked the flattery of attention.

The farmer paid William well and to his intense joy, on his

return to the farm, he found that all the harm that Bert had wrought had been remedied by William, and that all his agricultural interests were paying very well.

Bert was sent about his business, and then the trouble began in earnest.

Behind William's back he told all manner of tales, and once went so far as to slander Phyllis by compromising her name with William's. William went straight to his master.

'Do you believe this of me?' he demanded, in a serious and aggrieved tone.

'I do.'

'You believe him before me, 'Bor?'

'Yes,' replied the farmer.

'Well, all I can say is, you'm a bigger fule than I ever thought ye to be. I'm going away, now, and when you've made a mess of everything again or you'm ill, you can get Bert Isaac to help 'ee out. It'll be no use sending for me.' So saying, he went into the house and took his leave of the women, and then went away in St Benet's direction to a place called Lower Street, beyond Horning.

That night, whilst he was looking into the river with his heart in his mouth, he felt a hand on his sleeve, and turning quickly discovered Phyllis, white as death, gazing into his face.

'What's brought you here?' he asked, somewhat taken aback.

'I asked along the way the direction you had taken,' she replied, choking down a sob.

'Anything wrong?' he enquired, looking anxiously into her upturned eyes.

'A terrible row. I couldn't stand it any longer. Father and Bert. They came to blows. Father had been drinking, and Bert struck him and now he's unconscious. He may be dead by now, for all I know.'

'And Bert?'

'Oh, he's raving and is going to kill you if ever he meets you. Says you were the cause of the whole disturbance. Let's go away, Bill? Let's go. Let me come with you.'

'No, mawther, I can't allow this to go on. Your mother's in danger and your father may be dead. We'll go back. I will, anyway, and stop it all. Promise now, before God, you'll marry me.'

And the young girl promised by the light of the moon that she would wed William Ethelwistle and no other. They embraced, and for the first time he knew the loving caress of a woman's lips.

He went back and left Phyllis at a cottager's in the village street. The next morning he arrived at Sunny-Side Farm, went straight into the house, and met Bert in the passage.

'What do you want?' yelled Bert, directly he saw him.

'Not you,' replied William, quite calmly.

'Where's th' mawther?' shouted Bert, meaning Phyllis, for you may not know that is the Norfolk term for a young girl. 'You've got her somewhere.'

'Get out of my way,' said William, gently but firmly, pushing him aside.

'What do you want?' Bert yelled again, trying to stop him.

'I want fayther.'

'Well, you can want. He isn't here.'

'Where is he?'

'What's that to you?'

'Hey, get out of it.' replied William, giving him a swinging push aside, and making for the door in front of him.

'You can't go in there!' yelled Bert, hysterically. 'Don't go in there. Come back!' Seizing him by the coat collar William flung him away and went straight into the room, and there, lying across the hearth, was the dead body of the farmer. With a half-stifled cry he drew back and turning to Bert, said:

'Did you strike him down? Come here! Answer me!'

The craven youth stuttered and cried, wringing his hands and biting his lips:

'I didn't do it! I didn't do it!'

Of course the whole thing was self-evident, and before the police could arrive and take charge, Bert raced off across this long meadow in front of us now, stumbling and falling in his mad panic to get to the river. And there he hurled himself in. They saw him from the window commit his last act. He went down and never came up.

William went after Phyllis, brought her back, and when a decent time had elapsed, they were married at that church up on the hill over there in the trees, and lived in the old house for years and years.

'But what of the ghost? You haven't told me a word about him, dear friend,' I enquired anxiously, fearing he had forgotten all about it.

'Oh – ah – yes!' he replied. 'The ghost. We forgot all about the ghost, didn't we?'

'Yes, it's a terrible story, but about the ghost? Where does he come in? What does he do?'

'Oh,' he answered, rubbing his old chin. 'Well, that farmer is still wandering round about here looking for the feller what murdered him. Two or three times a month he comes by. He roams all round this meadow and stops and looks into the river, and then goes back to old Sunny-Side House.'

'What will he do when he does find him?' I enquired.

'Oh – why, murder him, of course.'

'You don't mean that, surely?' I asked, remembering that this all occurred so long ago.

'I most certainly do,' he replied, looking as though he resented my incredulity.

'But what makes you so definitely certain on that point.' I asked, controlling with an effort my risible faculties.

'Because,' and he leaned forward and breathed on me, 'I – am – the – murdered – man!'

In a flash I realised the poor chap was a lunatic, and before the words were scarcely completed, I threw my head back and laughed aloud. The laugh over, I turned to speak to him again, and to my unspeakable horror he was – GONE. Absolutely *gone!*

A cold shiver ran down my spine, my tongue clove to the roof of my mouth, and I gasped. He was nowhere in sight and there was

22

nowhere for him to hide in that wide open space. He could not have gone anywhere in that short moment without being seen. I strained my eyes in every possible direction but without avail. He was certainly no lunatic. Into invisibility he had vanished as he sat by my side, and when I only think of it I go stone cold. Whilst sitting with me and talking he was as much real flesh and blood as you or I, and yet – Ugh-r-r-r-rh. I can feel the cold wind blowing on my face at this moment as I tell you about it.

If ever you're up that way, and you see a man attending the cows, remember my awful experience and give him a miss.

Burgh Castle

And this is one of the many stories of Burgh Castle, hitherto un-recorded, but, nevertheless, as reliable and worthy of being chronicled as tradition can make it. It does not depend upon the ever-ready romanticism of the local indigénes for its existence, but boast an honoured acceptance down the pages of unwritten history, as indeed do so many of the events in historical chronology, more especially noticeable the farther one delves back into the realms of illiteracy and unlearning, when might was right and a King could do no wrong.

Gariannonum, as this fortress was named by the Romans, stood on a bluff at the extreme westward of what today is Breydon Water, and at the furthermost part of 'Lovingeland', later known as 'Lothing Land', and which gave its name to the beautiful lake of super-oriental peace and loveliness [sic], which lies between Oulton and Lowestoft. The foot commanded the entrance to the river Waveney on its right bank and its effluent into Breydon.

In those days Breydon Water was an estuary of the sea and received the rivers Bure, Yare and Waveney, and this arm of the Oceanus Germanicus was known as Gariannonum Ostium, meaning the mouth of the Yare, this particular river being regarded as worthy of precedence over the other two, probably on account of its navigability so far inland. This fortress was the second in importance of that chain of similar defences which the Romans erected on the Saxon Shore, i.e., that portion of our coast-line that was easiest of access to the Saxons and other raiders, who made our shores the objective of their repeated attentions. And so it comes about that this quiet, peaceful ruin, or rather relic, of ancient times, where today little girls and boys play at soldiering, have camps, and tell stories around their camp-fires, is saturated with the blood of the past, and at night strange things are said to happen there which will make the blood run cold, give you freezing shivers down the spine, and rivet you to the spot with your eyes bulging out of your head.

To appreciate fully the interest of what is about to be related,

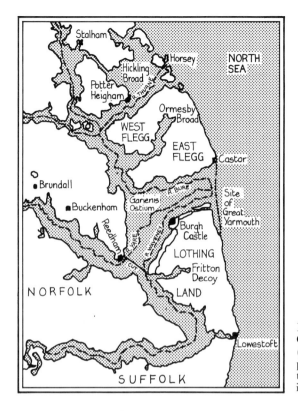

Map of
GARIANNONUM
(Burgh Castle) as it
probably was in Roman
times. The dotted lines
indicate the main rivers.

one must remember one or two important points and visualize Breydon Water open to the North Sea, because there was no Yarmouth at the time I am speaking of, and Caistor was the nearest sea-port to Burgh Castle, or Gariannonum. It was called Castor after one of the Roman gods, but what became of Pollux is not recorded.

A glance at the map on this page will explain far quicker than any writing the conditions which obtained in these parts in those early days, and give a fair idea of the contour of that part of the country at the time. This is taken from an old map in the possession of the Corporation of Great Yarmouth, and it shews very clearly the tidal waters of that period. The dotted lines indicate the rivers as we know them today. Castor, it will be noticed, stood at a mouth of the Yare which is now silted up, and Great Yarmouth is built on a silt bank from the three rivers Bure, Yare and Waveney, and a piled up island of shingle and sea-bed from the open sea. The Scrobey Sands, off Yarmouth, are a similar bank to that on which this pleasure resort stands.

25

Now for the story. In AD 418, when the Romans had gone home, this part of the coast became the scene of raids from overseas, and Jutes and Danes and Norsemen all contended in turn for its possession. Now it so happened that a band of Saxons and Angles, hearing of the success of their colonists in the 'North of the Humberland' area of Britain, decided to come across and colonise the more southerly parts, and landing on the East Coast somewhere in the region of Horsa Isle (Horsey) under Siberg, they took up their quarters all around that part, and later ventured down towards what today is Reedham. To their intense surprise they discovered that Gariannonum was occupied by their arch enemies the Danes, and one Gonard, a vaurien of the worst type, was in command.

Siberg had not come prepared for war, but peaceful as his intention of colonising was, he realised that the moment the Dane discovered their presence, war it would have to be; so he sent post haste to his brother in the North to come down and join forces with him, which he did, but not in time to prevent Gonard committing an infamous act of war against the settlers at Reedham, and butchering the entire community of four thousand. It will be easily understood that a messenger going North in those days might have to wander many miles after his arrival there to find the armies he was looking for. And so it happened that Cerdag, Siberg's half-brother, came to his aid exactly two months from the day the messenger left.

We must return to Siberg. A day or two after he had despatched his messenger to Cerdag, an ambassador arrived from Gonard requesting the pleasure of Siberg's presence, and all his people. Siberg went alone and unarmed, thinking that even Gonard would respect his defencelessness. But he was wrong and miscalculated the Dane completely. As soon as Siberg had set foot in Norfolk, Gonard knew of it, and that it was he, Siberg himself, who had come. He also knew that Siberg would not restrain the sword, and so in what he regarded as pure self-defence and protection, he laid his plans carefully, and everything went according to programme.

Siberg went back with the ambassador, but before leaving instructed his people that if he did not return in three days they were to come and fetch him, and with this feeling of mistrust he took his departure.

Gonard received him graciously, and almost haughtily, and when he learned of what Siberg had told his people to do in the event of his not returning to them within three days, he just clapped Siberg into irons, and flung him into a dungeon deep down almost to the bottom of the fortress' foundations, where scarce any light could enter and the floor was the playground for rats. Two men were posted at his prison door, and Siberg prayed hard for deliverance. On the fourth day, there was heard an immense clamour without, and the noise of battle resounded in every nook and cranny of the castle. The onslaught was so terrific that Gonard and his troops were somewhat scared of the consequences, and went to great pains to strengthen their resistance by every particle of ingenuity that wit and cunning could devise. At last, in a superhuman effort, he made a flank and rear attack at the same time. The Saxons fell like ninepins and scattered, but not far. They were brought down by a creeping barrage of arrows as they ran, and horses were sent out with chains to drag them, dead or alive into the fortress. Those that were already dead were fortunate. Those that were not were treated as though they were. Gonard surveyed the massacre with intense satisfaction. Not one escaped alive.

Whilst this superlative assassin dined in ecstasy that night, posts were being erected around the entire ramparts, copings and foreshore of the fortress, and by six the following morning each post carried its full burden of a naked human body cloven down the middle from the top of the head to the base of the trunk, with the halves kept open by pieces of stick, much the same as a modern butcher displays his mutton carcases, except in his case the viscera have always been removed. With Gonard this was not bothered about. No more sickening sight can humanly be imagined, to no baser level can anyone sink than that of the necrophilist, the ghoul who can wallow up to his armpits in human blood with an insensate joy of self-satisfaction, to no greater depth could any man sink who flattered his own vanity by mutilating the dead. That was Gonard, so well benamed the Vaurien Dane.

The entire fortress the next day was a human butchery, with four thousand human bodies exposed to view. Wherever you went, whichever way you looked, axed corpses hung on poles, partly as a warning to anyone else who might take it into their head to counter this arch-savage, this human tiger, this most loathesome and bestial of degenerate human porcinity. It was impossible that this terrific and ghastly holocaust of sheer bloody murder could carry through without someone or other getting away and spreading the awful news.

One of these Saxons, by name Beidasch, fled as he saw the turn of the battle, and made North in the hope that he could acquaint Cerdag who might be on his way.

And so it came about, as Gonard on the second day of his triumphant massacre was seated on the highest elevation rejoicing to himself as he gazed down upon the gruesome handiwork around him, his eye caught sight of a strange happening in mid-air, and he was rivetted to the spot. A large white angel was contending with a black one. Backwards and forwards they wrestled, then high into the air they soared, locked together, to fall again, toppling over one another as they fell. This way, then that, from side to side they flung each other violently, falling and rolling over one another in their strenuous endeavours to strangle the other. Then suddenly the white hands crept towards the black neck of its enemy, and gradually the large black head was pushed back and its throat was seized in the grip that would never relax until the last breath was out of the ugly, cruel black body. Down they came, tumbling and falling, the white, glistening hands never relaxing for an instant, and down and down and down they came until they struck the water with a huge splash just outside the castle at the Waveney entrance to Breydon. Then peace reigned once more, but Gonard was stupefied at what he had seen. He had never heard of angels, and could not conceive what such a vision could mean.

At first he was scared and decided to call his right-hand butcher to him and tell what he had witnessed, but the moment he considered it again, he knew that Propar would suspect him, and once he lost his confidence he might as well hand over the entire reigns of government. It was then he suddenly remembered that within the fortress there was one man who might explain what he had seen, and that was Siberg, for as far as he knew Siberg was still alive, languishing in the dungeon beneath the castle. Calling a soldier to his side he sent a message to Propar to despatch an armed guard down to the vaults and bring Siberg up to him.

In a few minutes there stood before him in chains the emaciated form of his prisoner, weak and dying for want of food and air. Then Gonard told him what he had seen and asked him if he could explain it. For answer Siberg merely indicated that he could not speak whilst in chains and surrounded by others, so Gonard, satisfied that he had nothing to fear from this starving, broken victim of his malice, caused his fetters to be removed, the guard to leave them, and a stoup of wine to be brought. Siberg swallowed the wine and new life coursed through his veins, but he took good care not to let it be noticed. Gonard took his long-handled axe from his belt, tested its edge with his thumb and laid it before him, perhaps as a threat to his prisoner, then commanded Siberg to gaze around at the display of the dead about the fortress. The air was laden with the sickening smell of death, and even Siberg's eyes swam with moisture as his vision fell upon the remains of his beloved followers.

'Now,' exclaimed this brutal tyrant, 'speak and tell me the

meanings of this thing! Men with wings who fly as birds I have never seen before, neither have I heard of them. Speak, I command you!'

A sickly smile stole across his victim's face, and in a coarse, viperous snap, Gonard shouted at him:

'Would you deride me, even now as my prisoner?' and leering forward at Siberg, he spat in his face. By a superhuman effort Siberg remained unmoved.

'Answer me, you swine,' yelled Gonard, tugging violently at his prisoner's clothes. For answer Siberg smiled calmly and quietly, and then, gently raising his arm he pointed to the horizon around, and Gonard's eyes beheld something that made his blood freeze. Everywhere he looked the land was black with people, all concentrating on Gariannonum. The Ostium was black with hundreds of ships, the Yare was full, the Waveney was full, and the castle was beset on all sides. With a look of petrified fear, Gonard cried out:

'What does all this mean?'

Then for the first time Siberg spoke to him.

'That,' said he quite calmly, 'is the host of Cerdag, my brother, coming to avenge the massacre of his brother's people.'

Gonard turned, and only for an instant, to satisfy himself that what he had seen was really true, but in that moment, quicker almost than the mind can think, Siberg had snatched up the axe, and when it had fallen, he picked up the human mask of his persecutor by the fringe of hair on its forehead, and holding it at arm's length towards the surging hordes who were fast approaching, exclaimed:

'See once more, you vaurien coward, you merciless brute. See again the people you have massacred.' The body of Gonard, sightless, faceless and jawless, rolled in anguish at the feet of Siberg. It could hear, but it could not see. It writhed and twisted like some helpless, unfortunate dogfish, lashing out in its agony and clawing the ground in its relentless suffering. Twice it tried to rise, but fell back unable to erect itself, 'auffing' in its throat as it choked itself with blood. The guards raced up as soon as they realised what had happened and were confronted with the life-mask of their chief held towards them by Siberg, who pointed to the seething masses approaching the fortress. They stopped, spellbound, then comprehending in a flash the importance and gravity of their position, they had no longer any thought for Gonard or Siberg, but fled precipitously in different directions, blowing their horns to summon the entire fort. Propar, the murderous butcher, bothered nothing about Siberg, but took command immediately the news of Gonard reached him,

had the cattle and sheep brought into the castle and all those working in the fields, and the gates closed against the oncoming host.

In a short while Cerdag reached the outer confines of the castle, and there his army saw the remains of his brother's colonials. He sent a messenger to the castle with a white flag, demanding the immediate surrender of the entire army, and stating that not one of them could escape, as the fort was encompassed on all sides.

For reply, the dead body of his emissary was flung from one of the parapets with the white flag tied around his neck in a strangle-knot. Cerdag had received his answer.

Preparations were immediately made for an assault. Huge tree trunks were brought on wheels and with long ropes were pulled by scores of willing hands under cover of their shields in Roman tortoise fashion. It did not take long to ram the great gates off their hinges, and then the hand-to-hand fighting began. In their hundreds and thousands the invaders surged into this hell-hole of infamy and assassination. Up along the ramparts raced the men of Cerdag down the bays and traverses, along the copings and down the stairs, first this way then that; it was a terrific battle. Not one was spared.

Every living soul in that fortress was put to the sword, and then

Cerdag, standing on the highest point of Burgh Castle, gazing around over the peaceful plains and listening to the wild clamour of unabated excitement amongst his people below, heard a deep sigh come from someone close at hand. He went over to where it appeared to come from, and stepped over a faceless body in doing so. And there, behind a stone turret, half leaning, half dropping, was his brother Siberg, dying from an arrow, which still stood embedded in his side, and in his hand he still clutched the face of Gonard. Siberg recognised his brother, and Cerdag drew out the weapon, staunched the bleeding, dressed the wound, and taking his cloak he wrapped it around his brother and had him carried below. But Siberg slowly sank, and later died in his brother's arms.

'Oh, would that arrow had been other than mine!' he cried, as Siberg looked up into his loving eyes, and then closed his own in sleep. Cerdag interred him where he had found him, on the highest part of the castle wall, with his grim trophy still in his hand.

And that is the story of Burgh Castle. On 27 April, every year and just before dawn, the assassination of Siberg's men takes place. When it is scarcely light, the clang of arms in deadly conflict and the yells of men in battle ring out across those peaceful meads and the tranquil waters of Breydon.

On 3 July, as regularly as clockwork, the dead body of a man with a white flag tied tightly round his neck comes hurtling through the air from the precincts of the castle as though fired from a balista machine. It falls on the foreshore with a sickening thud and disappears. These visions have been witnessed and heard by many persons of unimpeachable reliability, and their records are to be found in the transactions of several learned societies who deal with antiquities.

Only twice has the fight between the two angels been seen and recorded. The first time it was seen by a learned doctor who lived at Buckenham close by, many years ago, somewhere in the late 'forties, and on the second occasion it was witnessed by a priest of Westminster Cathedral, on 26 June 1905, when he was on a short holiday in those parts with a member of the author's family.

It is common knowledge that Burgh Castle reflects its original self in the early morning mists of May, complete with all its ramparts, bastions, gates, redoubts, and turrets, as when it was first built, and the banner of the regiment of Stablesian Horse floated above its central tower.

'Praep. equitum Stablesianorum Gariannonensium, Gariannono.' (vide, *Notitia Dignitatum*).

And that must be the best part of two thousand years ago.

Salhouse

Dear little Salhouse,
Haven of perpetual peace,
How serene are your waters!
Thy calm reigns supreme,
Thy restful tranquility
Nought will disturb.
And down through the ages
Thy lovers will say:
Dear little Salhouse,
Sweet little Salhouse,
We are coming again!
           – Brendon

And so sang the poet of one of the quietest little meres in Norfolk. As you enter from the Bure at either end, you are struck by its peaceful atmosphere, its silence and its repose. There are one or two boats about, and over there is a relic of the Great War, an M.L. now half sunk. The timbered slopes with their green swards that come right down to the banks give the whole Broad a distinct appearance from any other, and almost make one feel that one is in a theatre and that presently our eyes may be delighted with some delicious pastoral play in which the characters, in Plantagenet costume will transport us back to the days of the Angevin Kings. Gazing enraptured at the beauty of the scene, we can almost people the slopes with medieval lovers, a kept tryst, a baronial banquet spread on tables beneath the trees, a royal Richard with his hunting party, or the small green pasture with a kingly cerf peacefully browsing, then raising its branching antlers at the sound of the distant horn. The baying of the dogs is heard; we see the glint of uncertainty in his large round and wondering eyes, and the regal stag's hasty departure as a pack of bloodhounds burst in upon the sacred quiet of this verdant solitude.

Dear little Salhouse, garden of the imagination, what stories you could tell, what wondrous episodes are locked up in the bosom of thy memory! But let us wait for the third Tuesday in May, and we shall see what midnight will bring to us.

At the end of the Broad is a small lagoon, called Salhouse Pool, and it is here that the story you are now going to hear is re-enacted every year, and has been so for six centuries.

Close by where the little farm now stands, there once stood a fine old stone manor with battlements and turrets, and it was here lived the famous and knightly family of Chassagne, directly descended from the royal standard-bearer to William, Duke of Normandy, le grand Marquis Raoul de Chassagne, Comte du Frontagnois, Chevalier du Cordon d'Or de Provence, Grand Maréchal du Banneret Sacré de Normandie, and Gardien Distingué des Reliques Sacrés des Grandes Armées.

When this Norman noble received the barony and moiety of the Manor of Salhouse in the Contrie of the North-folk, as a mark of his august Monarch's appreciation of his loyalty, the new English baron settled down to a quiet life to enjoy a well-earned rest which he sadly needed after all his battles abroad, and finally on English soil. And so it came about that Mons. le grand Marquis Raoul de Chassagne, having selected the site for his new manor and approved the design of it, the walls soon began to rise, the roof went on, the flag of the war-lord floated above the battlements, and told the countryside that their new lord of the manor was in residence.

The natives in that area were filled with apprehension at the new life that was opening out for them, and if gossip ran high, speculation rose higher. All kinds of divers rumours sprung into existence, and at last the tenantry of the new lord convened a meeting and appointed delegates to wait upon the Baron, to place their position before him and learn the worst.

My lord Raoul de Chassagne received them in the large banqueting hall, and kneeling at his feet as he sat on the dais under the minstrel gallery, they told him all that was feared, and begged his clemency and consideration, in return for which they assured him of their unswerving loyalty.

The Baron listened astounded. Such thoughts that had worried his people had never occurred to him, and after a short while, and the gravity of the situation having revealed itself, he leaned back and laughed so good-naturedly that the simple-minded delegates were almost alarmed, and exchanged looks with each other that left no doubt as to their mystified anxiety.

Clapping his hands for an attendant, he ordered wine to be brought, and the order obeyed, they clanked their drinking horns, and the Baron said:

'Go back to my good and worthy people, convey them tidings of great joy, and ask their prayers for me. Hold! This day week shall be a holiday, the park shall be opened to my people, and I pray that you all attend my Mass on the lake at midnight, and breakfast with me at ten of the clock in the garden.'

The delegates thanked him and returned to the people, who received the news with great rejoicing.

During the week, great preparations were made for the feast. Triumphal arches of evergreen were built on all the roads entering the park, and a huge raft made by lashing several lighters together was moored in the Pool. On this raft was erected an Altar, gorgeously decorated, and priceless silken carpets from the East were laid on the deck. The sides of the raft were obscured with rich hangings in white and gold, and cloth of gold curtains hung at the back and sides of the Altar.

On the big lawn in front of the Manor were trestle-tables, and carpenters were busy knocking-up forms to seat the people.

On the eve of the midnight Mass, boats of all kinds began to arrive from different places around, and by eleven p.m. the Pool was full, and the banks were crowded. Not only the Baron's immediate tenantry, but the news having spread very quickly, people from the outlying districts had poured in.

At half-past eleven a procession started from the Manor, headed

by a company of pikemen, followed by a crucifer and six acolytes in red cassocks and beautiful lace rochets. Then came a choir of men and boys in similar garb, chanting the Psalms. Following close behind came two thurifers swinging their censers, and two small boat-bearers carrying the incense. After these came twelve priests in dalmatics and chasubles, then the new Lord Abbot of St Benet's Priory which had been partially rebuilt, then four monsignori in their rich copes, and next to them came my Lord Bishop of Norwiche in cope and mitre carrying his crozier, whilst the lord Raoul de Chassagne in full Norman armour and carrying his helm, walked behind, followed by another company of soldiers. Torch-bearers walked at the sides of the procession, as it wended its way down to the lake-side, and, on arriving there, the bishop and abbot and several priests with torch-bearers, acolytes, thurifers and crucifer walked over a little bridge of boats to the now illuminated raft, and there the ceremony of robing the bishop for his episcopal Mass was proceeded with. The choir of boys assembled themselves on the right side of the lake, and another choir of little girls all in white formed up on the left, and during the preliminary ceremony of robing the celebrant and dressing the Altar, the two choirs rendered the Canticle of Canticles alternately.

It was a magnificent night, the moon was full, and high in the heavens, not a cloud was to be seen, and not a zephyr stirred the leaves on the trees. The air was mild and balmy, and everybody was standing in silent reverence.

Presently the bishop ascended the Altar steps, and the Mass began. It might be truthfully said that no such Mass had ever been said before or since in England. The incense drifted away in flat clouds across the kneeling multitude, and when the bishop turned and bestowed the episcopal benediction, the Baron laid aside his sword and casque, and knelt at his feet. A great shout of praise went up as the Te Deum was sung by the choirs, and was taken up by the people, the procession re-formed, and the Baron with his retinue returned to the Manor.

The emotion at this service was very marked all round, and the ritual was so holy and impressive that even hardened men were seen to weep. The six large candles on the Altar were kept alight, and the Host was left exposed in a gilt monstrance with a relic of the True Cross above the Tabernacle in the centre of the Altar, and a company of archers with drawn bows kept guard around the Altar steps.

The following morning at ten of the clock, servants by the score, bearing the choicest meats, soups and vegetables, and large puddings, came out and laid them on the tables. Foaming tankards of rich brown ale were placed by each bowl – there were no plates in those days – and as soon as the Lord Abbot of St Benet's had blessed the assembly and then the food, the people sat down and feasted right royally. Six huge barons of beef were roasted whole on spits over wood fires, and the boys with the basting ladles worked like niggers. Sizzling meats were heaped in the people's bowls, and they fell to with one accord. There were the roast beef, and roast mutton, venison pies, wild-duck, capons, pigeons, hares, and above all, bustards roasted in wet clay and stuffed with mulberries. The tables were laden with luscious fruits and sweets of all kinds, nuts and raisins. The red Normandie wine flowed like water, and the worthy people, never having tasted it before, soon found life most agreeable, and some spoke to each other quite happily who had not spoken for years. Every village and hamlet has its petty estrangements, but Normandie grape appeared to dissolve all differences.

After the feast the Baron addressed his people and told them they had nothing to fear, and that he had set his determination on helping them to improve themselves in the ways they had always been accustomed, and that it was not his intention to interfere with their methods of life in any way whatsoever, and that all males capable of bearing arms would be expected to serve for three months in his band of armed retainers.

Following this sumptuous banquet, there was Maypole dancing, and then some 'Mawrish' dancing performed by the Baron's own retainers, who had travelled abroad with him and learned its curious movements in the Near East. Then followed games for everybody. From tiny mite to sturdy wight, everyone joined in the competitions. There were running races, weight-throwing, quarter-staff, tugs-of-war, and follow-my-leader, in which everybody, both big and small, joined in and processed to the plaintive pleading of quaint pipe music. Everyone was happy, not a sad face was to be seen anywhere, and even the old granfers sat around and smiled and nodded their bewhiskered approval.

My Lord Bishop of Norwiche, wearing his purple soutane and gold pectoral cross, came down after breakfast amongst the merrymakers and walked in their midst. He was accompanied by the Baron Raoul with his eldest son, a youth of sixteen. The Baron spoke excellent English, because, as a boy, he had been to school for some years in the grammar school of the ancient monastery of the Benedictines near Sarum. His magnanimity took him straight to the hearts of his people, and in a little while they had grown to love him and swear fealty to his house and standard.

The evening closed in with bonfires and more dancing on the lawn, and by nine of the clock the visitors had all departed, the last boat was gone, and night settled down on this happy spot, wrapping it in its soft mantle of gentle fragrance with only the faintest zephyrs soughing through the topmost branches of the trees.

And so ended the happiest day in all the chronicles of Salhouse, and every 13th of May this day is repeated with all its joys and happiness. It is only mete and fitting that such rejoicing should travel down through the pages of history, and that the joys and pleasures of this memorable feast of Baron Raoul should perpetuate itself through the ages. Though the Manor has long since passed into decay and oblivion and the family of Chassagne ceased to exist for hundreds of years, yet the memorable exultation of that triumphant revel has come down through the mists of the past, showing that the spiritual in life carries on when stones have ceased to speak.

And so, on the night of the 12th, and 13th day of the Month of Flowers, if you are in Salhouse Pool and keep very quiet, you will certainly hear the chantings of the choirs coming as it were through the trees, and maybe, if you are at all attuned with psychic matters and not hostile to them, you may actually attend the midnight episcopal Mass celebrated by my Lord Bishop of Norwiche. It has been witnessed by five different people in the last thirty years. One, the principal of Mary's College, Oxford, in 1903, wrote in the University journal *Isis* a description of it.

'It was most impressive,' he said, 'more impressive than anything I have ever seen. It was so real that I felt I had actually attended divine worship.'

Another man, a scientist of the first order, the great Professor Alexander Jardine, of Cambridge University, records having witnessed the entire phenomenon both in 1899 and in 1900. Here is the testimony of a man which must be accepted, and *he* told me.

'Do you know, sir, it had an extraordinary effect upon me. I never was religious, or even inclined that way, but it produced in me a peculiar reverential awe for the first time in my life when I first saw it, and affected me so I had to go the following year to verify it, because I refused even to believe that I had seen it myself. I fancied after a while that my mind had suddenly taken a new turn, and that I was becoming a dreamer, that my day dreams were pure phantasies, and that if I allowed myself to give in to them I should become unbalanced. My second visit in 1900 convinced me that this was no hallucination of a mind fatigued, but rather the tapping-in on a wavelength of mental energy that allowed me to re-witness the scenes that were re-enacted every year.

'Remember, nothing is lost in the realm of energy. Once vibrations in the ether are sent out they continue for ever or until they find impact in some restraining agency.'

The London Metaphysical League investigated and reported on this as late as 1923, and their President, Dr Leon Berkeley, adds his testimony to the numbers of people who have witnessed it. The learned professor, in the Transactions of the League, reports in Vol. 17, Chapters 39 and 40, on pages 217–60, as follows:

'I made a special visit in order to test for myself the story of this phenomenon which had come to me. In company with four of my colleagues from the Technicological Laboratory of the League, all doctors of science and hard men to convince of anything supernormal, we journeyed down to Horning, where we procured a small motor-launch, and in the early evening of the 12th May "pulled in" to Salhouse Pool, made ourselves snug, and awaited the coming of the manifestation. At 11.30 p.m. precisely it began. It was a very dark night and we were the only people in the little pool. The air was still, and presently we were able to make out a large number of boats and crafts of extraordinary shape all around us, and the people in them in their mediæval garb of the period. Although they were all quite excited, yet not a sound disturbed the tranquillity of the moment. Presently the ringing of small hand-bells did actually make themselves heard, and there, down the grassy slope in front of the little farmhouse, wended a torchlight procession. It was very dim, but quite easily discernible. High dignitaries of the Church, including a mitred abbot, companies of soldiers in Norman uniforms came down to the water-side, and then several of the processors left the promenation and walked across what appeared to be a small bridge of boats to a huge floating Altar, which had just become visible in the centre of the pool. It was gorgeously decorated with cloth of gold and very white fine linen. Burning tapers on six massive silver candlesticks, each as tall as a six-foot man, flickered and shed their soft lights upon the ceremonies we witnessed take place in that open sanctuary.

'Choirs of men and boys and little girls sang lustily, but although they were quite close their sounds seemed to be ever so distant, yet clear. The rites and rituals of the Roman Mass were meticulously performed, and when the celebrant had pronounced the episcopal benediction, he and the others returned to the shore by the little pontoon-bridge, the procession re-formed and, wending its way back up the grassy slope, slowly faded out into nothingness amidst the trees.

'One by one the lights from the torch-bearers flickered out, and on looking around, we realised once more that we were alone, the boats around us had disappeared, and all the people on shore had gone as well. Then the moon came up from behind a cloud and we gazed at each other amazed at what we had just seen.'

It is a wonderful phenomenon, and those who are sensitive to psychic vibrations should not miss it.

The one point which to my mind makes this so specially interesting is, that it dispels the popular idea that ghosts are of necessity always of evil origin, and portend disaster. The midnight Mass on Salhouse has, on the contrary, quite a reassuring effect upon all who witness it, and they are many, dispelling fear, allaying apprehension, and soothing the mind with a mental peace that brings blessings and happiness to all those fortunate enough to be present.

Those who venture must not be disappointed if their first attempt is unsuccessful, as success must depend entirely on the person himself. Three men of my acquaintance went down to Salhouse five years ago on 12 May. Two of them saw the whole manifestation, while the third, who tried hard, saw nothing.

It is, nevertheless a wondrously beautiful spectacle, and well worth trying to see.

Breydon Water

Times change and some places change with them, to wit this sinister stretch of water, which lies between Great Yarmouth and Reedham and Burgh Castle. It is difficult to look back and picture its shores washed by the bounding main with ships of many nations coming and going, and the blue horizon of the ocean stretching across where now is land from Caistor to Gorleston. Nevertheless, it is true, because all that meadow land from Reedham to Caistor was part of the sea, and fairly deep, too, for large vessels came right up to Reedham and St Olaves. Breydon Water in A D 400 was an estuary receiving the effluents of the Gare (Yare), Bure and Waveney, and as it offered a common Mouth for these three rivers, it was named after the first and most important one and called Garienis Ostium. A glance at the map on page 25 will easily explain what it was like in those days, and so, having introduced its ancient aspect, let us now return to the twentieth century and hear the story of Breydon Water as told to me by Admiral Sir John Haven-Gore, Bt., K.C.V.O., G.C.M.G., K.C.S.I., D.S.O.

The author's motor yacht *Whitelady* was lying at St Olaves when the gallant Admiral came alongside, and right glad we were to see him, for 'H.-G.' as he was affectionately called by his intimates, is always a refreshing sight, and a better raconteur it would be hard to find, so listen to the Admiral's narration:

No, I don't like Breydon, skipper. Neither would you if you had been with me on the night of 11 July last year (1929). You know I'm a very keen fisherman, and every year I try out a new place. Last year I decided to fish on Breydon, and accordingly rented that little black hutch of a fishing float which you jocularly described in your cruise of 1930 in *The Yachtsman* last autumn. It is generally moored on the North Flats, rather to the westward, and at the mouth of the Fleet Dyke which comes down from South Walsham Marshes, which, by the way, is nothing to do with the South Walsham of Broad fame, and also possesses a Fleet Dyke which runs into Ward Marsh and the river Bure, just above St Benet's Abbey.

It was merely a large packing-case on a float, with a stove and a

40

stack-pipe, and just room for two persons to lie out comfortably. At low water she sits flat on the mud, and at high tide she swings to her chains with all the self-satisfied composure of a houseboat at Bray. One night we pushed off in the dinghy and left a lighted lantern on the roof as a guide against our return, because the night was as black as Hades. We rowed over to a spot about a hundred yards from where the Dyke falls into the deep water, and 'throwing over', lighted our lantern, baited our hooks and lowered our leads to the bottom. It was a warm, balmy night with a clear sky and I remember how my man and I gazed up at the bow of Perseus and Casseopœa, and he asked me to tell him something about them. I was just re-counting the old Greek legend of Andromeda and Perseus, and 'feeling' the ground with my sinker, when suddenly both he and I became aware of a great noise approaching us from a distance. It was the tumult of several thousand voices raised in exultation, and then, although the night was still dark, the air became gradually illuminated by a strange phosphorescence creeping through the water and com-ing towards us. It was as though a silvery dawn was slowly spreading across the inland sea and approaching nearer as the resounding noise increased. It came as it were from across the meads in a nor'-easterly direction, from between Caistor and Yarmouth. In a short

while the phosphorescence had spread right round and beyond our dinghy, and we could actually see our lines on the bottom, the water had become so clear.

Louder and louder became the noise and presently there loomed up the luminescent forms of scores of large sailing galleons crowded with soldiers and rowers. Although there was no wind their sails were full, but one's face experienced the feeling of cold as though a wind were blowing upon it, and yet there was none. On they came, and as they neared us, we could make them out quite easily.

They were without any question, from far over the sea, and there must have been thousands aboard those ships. Everyone appeared to be rejoicing and singing and shouting, long bannerets fluttered from their mains, and lights flickered in various parts of the vessels. Oil burned brightly in their huge castle lanterns, and as they swarmed by they did not see us. On their bellying sails were huge emblems of the sun, mystical cuboid designs, and long, very long pennants floated out from their trucks. Near the tops of the masts were large crow's-nests, like fighting-tops, and full of men. Their shrouds were full of armed people and all were excited as could be. Away behind them more ships still came on, but with greater distances between them, and where once had been the meads was now definitely the open sea, and it glistened and shimmered as it would in a strong moonlight, but – there was no moon in the sky. Where they could be going it was impossible even to surmise.

One large vessel came quite close to us; in fact she seemed to be bearing right down upon us, her ponderous bow, spreading and bulging like a Dutch barge, was simply ploughing its way through the water at a terrific pelt. As they went past and only just missing us, we hailed them, and several on board must have heard us, because they came, and looking over the side, stared in our direction, but although we could have touched them with our boat-hook, they could not see us.

That they belonged to another world was self-evident, and we were without doubt invisible to them.

Another curious thing about them was this, that although they disturbed the water and made huge waves, and left behind quite an unpleasant lop for a small boat like ours, yet their undulations never moved us, and we remained, as it were, in still water all the while. They all passed along in the direction of the Waveney and Burgh Castle, and, as the last ship followed on, so the luminescence of the sea closed in behind them leaving the darkness in their wake.

All this happened just before midnight, and lasted quite an hour and a half. About four bells the moon did actually come up and was full, enabling us to see, almost as clearly as in daylight, and curious to relate, the sea had gone and was now replaced once more by the meads, whilst the sea horizon had given place to trees and distant houses.

Who were they? What were they? And when were they? These are the questions which rise immediately and call for answer. Well, what I have to say is only a suggestion and may be quite wrong; still it is worthy, if you will allow me, of your consideration. The ships were Teutonic in type, and favoured, I should say, the fifth and sixth centuries; so were they Saxon invaders, or Anglo-Saxon Colonials? Further than that, it is impossible to hazard even a guess. They were a noisy crowd whoever they were.

Now, on referring to historical records we learn that two famous Saxon chiefs did actually arrive with their armies from over-seas, and that was in AD 447, and that Elle or Ella landed somewhere on the east coast at the same time as Cissa landed on the south coast, and made the old Roman city of Regnum his centre, renaming it after himself Cissacæstra (Chichester).

The question which now confronts us is whether this could be Elle's landing in Britain over and over again, because many people have seen it, and in the *Gentlemen's Gazette* of August 1671, it is mentioned clearly and without hesitation. I knew nothing about this landing until after I had seen it, and then decided to lighten my darkness and read it up. I am aware my suggestion takes the line of least resistance in seeking an explanation, concluded the Admiral, but can you think of a simpler or a better one?

I was so interested in the Admiral's story that I asked 'Orace, at the Yacht Station at Great Yarmouth, if he had ever heard that Breydon Water was haunted.

'Haunted?' he replied, looking aghast at me. 'What do 'ee know about it?'

'Nothing', I answered, toying with discretion.

'Been hearin' things, eh?' he enquired, with the delicious but unwitting sneer so particularly his.

'I was only wondering, that's all. It looks as though it could be.' no knowledge of anything, and seeing an opportunity to impose his own, he remarked:

'Come in and sit down, and I'll tell 'ee all about it. It's an ugly place at best o' times. Lots o' people go out there and never comes back no more. Haunted? I should just think it were.' I interrupted him, and he continued:

'Me? What, me afeered o' ghosts? Don't be silly. O' course not;

43

but that don't say as I don't b'lieve in 'em, 'cos arter all, seein' is believin', as the sayin' goes. Yes, I've seen the big black ship with the skulls and cross-bones on her main course, but they don't like speakin' about her round this way. Come 'ere now, and listen to this:

'One night last summer two years back, me and George Sharples, of Caistor over yonder, went out on Breydon to do a bit o' fishin'. We was doin' very well lyin' just off the old Fleet Dyke, if you know it and I don't suppose you do, when George says to me, "'Orace!" he says, "I've got a uncomfortable feelin' as somethin's goin' to 'appen. The words was no sooner out of 'is mouth than somethin' did 'appen. 'Ere listen to me a minute and never mind yer pipe. 'Ave you ever broke out into a cold sweat, 'ad icy-cold water run all down yer spine till you was sittin' in a puddle o' water and enough ter give yer the pneumoniers, an' your knees knockin' together like clappers and your teeth chatterin' like a ratchet? 'Ave you? I'm arskin' yer. Then somethin' blows across yer face, you feels cold, wet 'ands on your cheeks, and yer stomick rolls over like a 'arf-filled balloon? If you 'aven't, then you don't know what it's like. Well, anyway, that's what 'appened to me. The night was so dark, and that made it worse. If George felt worse'n I did, then it's a wonder 'e survived.

'We looked around, in the direction that a muffling sort o' noise was comin' from, and then slowly there loomed up – oh, Gawd, it makes me feel terrible even to think of! It makes me blood run cold, and sets me all a tremblin' – I can see 'er now, comin' up out of the darkness like a towering great jet black bird, with 'er wings all spread out, and the most villainous lookin' crew lookin' at us over 'er rails. You never see such a lot of dirty ruffians in your life, all stripped to the waist with just a pair of ragged trousers on and their great, heavy, hairy chests all exposed. Their great arms all muscle and black hair made 'em look like a pack o' monkeys. Gorillas more'n likely. They peered at us as though we was difficult to see, and the stink what come with 'em nigh on choked us. I can smell it now. Like something burnin', what got you by the throat and made your eyes smart. She come along with a bow-wave big enough to swamp a little packet like us a hundred times over and not see us in the foam.

Then we see two smaller ships comin' up in the opposite direction to meet 'er, and they was packed stiff with soldiers in steel helmets and armour. Then presently there was a bit o' circlin' by them all, and presently one of the littler ones puts a shot across the big black 'un, and she replied. In a little while I knew somethin' was about to 'appen, an' it did. They closed in together, and then we see two great

44

red-'ot shots connected by a bit o' chain tear the big Jolly Roger's sail away and cut one set o' shrouds clean out of 'er.

'Then the littler ones, coming up alongside, threw grapplin' irons and jumped on to the deck of the big black ship. Then the yellin' and the shoutin' began. You never 'eard such a racket. Men was fightin' for their lives and you could 'ear plain as anyfing the cries o' the dyin'. They fought all over the ship, not only on the decks, but they was scrappin' on the bulwarks, in the shrouds, and one man I see with me own eyes flung out of a fightin'-top. I can see him fallin' now, an' almost hear him scream.

'What a fight! They used to put up the "rough stuff" all right in them days and they weren't afraid of hard knocks neither. It was a hand-to-hand business every time, and man for man as the sayin' goes. The fight lasted half-an-hour and we watched it all, and the air was thick with the smell of hot blood and the ringing clashings of steel. Men on the bulwarks wrostlin' for their lives fell overboard in their death grips, and disappeared in the muddy water around, and the sickening sight grew worse as the scrap went on. At last we see the whole lot suddenly fade out, the moon come up, and there wasn't no trace of nothing what 'ad just been takin' place.

'Haunted? If you don't believe me, ask old George Sharples and 'e'll tell 'ee "Yes" or "No". 'Underds o' people 'as seen what we seed that evening of the 14th September. Year arter year it 'appens just as I've told 'ee, but don't you go tellin' others 'bout it, or I'll be pestered to death by 'em.

'Last year, all through George not keeping 'is tongue still, a cinermatic feller come down to do a spot of "shootin'", as they call it, but 'e got nothin' for it were a bright moonlight night, and them fly-by-nights don't like bein' seen by me nor you, as the saying is.'

In the Transactions of the Metaphysical League this sea-fight is chronicled as taking place in many harbours. One specially favoured spot is in Plymouth Sound, just outside the Cattewater, where the same three ships have been seen in mortal combat many times.

The skipper of this death ship is one John King, who held a letter of marque in the seventeenth century, became a privateer, and then, ignoring his sovereign who granted him his commission, went off on his own. With his cut-throat crew, he evidently saw the advantages, even in those days, of running his outlawry on a co-operative basis, and became a buccaneer. He scoured the Spanish Main, and lay in wait for the 'Spanish Silver Fleet', as it was called, that carried bullion and jewels from the West Indies at definite times of the year.

It is also said that this is the same John King who 'comes through' at so many spiritualistic séances and is such a noisy person. You can always recognise him by his huge bullying, shouting and raucous voice. I have heard him many times and in different places. You would think it was a double-barrel voiced sergeant-major crooning through a megaphone to his young, but I know of no single occasion when he has revealed himself in person.

Still, if you're anywhere near Breydon Water next summer about 11 July or 14 September, keep a good lookout, and if we meet, we'll compare notes.

Barton

It is a wonderful experience to feel yourself floating on the waters of a haunted lake, and feeling that any minute something may happen to chill your marrow and turn your blood into blue custard, if you have any. But that will not happen on Barton Water, because the lady in question who has made this delectable expanse of loveliness her spiritual home is really a very charming young person. She is not only goodly to feast the eyes upon, but is a beneficent benefactor to all those who have the good fortune to see her, for she brings happiness to those in need, and blessings to their lines when angling, and that is the reason why Barton Broad is so alluring, so attractive, and so satisfying. She might almost be regarded as the Spirit of Contentment, for peace reigns upon those waters, and when you run into them from the wiggly little River Ant, it is like going into some beautiful and impressive place of worship, and one feels one wants to speak only in a whisper.

Barton Broad is about one hundred and thirty acres in extent, and there is not too much water anywhere, so care has to be taken not to pile up, or great difficulty will be found in getting 'off' again. There is about eight to ten feet of water in some parts, and it is very reedy in places. It is these reeds that play an important part in the 'ghost' of Barton Broad, as you will see.

It was in September 1916, that Flight-Lieutenant Ronald Jacoby, when flying over this mere about five o'clock one evening, happened to look down from his cockpit and saw to his intense surprise the face of a beautiful girl mirrored, as it were, in the water beneath. He could scarcely believe his eyes, more especially as the face turned in his direction as he passed over it. He said nothing about it, for fear of bringing ridicule upon himself from the rest of his squadron at Pulham, where he was stationed. The following day he made the same trip and saw her again. According to his own description 'she was even more beautiful than the "Lady of Shalott", but a very magnified edition, filling nearly the whole area of the larger portion of the Broad.'

So impressed was he, that one day he took his squadron leader with him on some pretext or other, and on arriving over the lake, told him to look down. The officer in question did so, and suddenly exclaimed 'My God!' On looking around at his passenger the pilot saw that he had turned deathly white, and enquired what was wrong.

'Have you seen it?' gasped the squadron leader.

'Seen what?' replied the pilot.

'Her! The face! The woman!' replied the other, trying to pull himself together.

'What *are* you talking about?'

'The face in the lake below', answered the leader, excitedly.

'What face? You haven't told me?' answered the pilot.

'No – no – you wouldn't understand. Sorry old man. It's all right. I shall be better presently.'

When they had returned to their station, the pilot enquired of his passenger, in the mess, what he meant and what had so upset him.

'My dear Jacoby, you wouldn't understand it. No one could but those who have seen it. Have a drink?'

'No, thanks', replied Jacoby, 'but tell me. I'm curious. Did you see something very horrible?'

'On the contrary, my dear boy', replied the other, 'she was too lovely for anything.'

'She? Who?'

'Why, the girl.'

'What girl?'

'Oh, sit down and I'll tell you all about it.'

They did so, and then the squadron leader told him what he had seen. 'But', he added, 'you won't tell anyone about this, or I'd be fired. You see, no one would believe but that I was suffering from hallucinations. And I swear on my oath to you, it – she – was nothing of that.'

'I'm glad you've seen it. Because——'

'What? Have you seen it, too?'

'Yes. And that was why I asked you to accompany me today, for if you saw it as well, then I know it could be nothing of my own imagination.'

'For the love of Mike, not a word of this to any living soul, Jacoby.'

It was Jacoby himself who first told me about this vision, and that he had tried to see it from low down but failed, and that above six hundred it was also invisible. It can only be seen at from four-fifty to six hundred feet up, and then just before the sun begins to dip in the west, and it was this that caused me to make up my mind to investigate this curious and beautiful phenomenon. Accordingly I went to Barton Broad in the *Whitelady* and cruised around in an earnest

48

endeavour to elucidate the mystery. Of the twenty people I interviewed there, who, having lived all their life in the vicinity, could be regarded in consequence as fairly reliable authorities, only two persons would venture to speak of it. One of these, Joe Barnes, shook his old head wisely, and said:

'' 'Bor, leave it alone. T'ant no gude to you nor me. I remember me ole faither tellin' me o' th' young mawther of the Broad, an' a-warnin' me never to go near the waters after sun-down.' Then he reamed off the following story that had come down in his family.

In the days of the Crusades, a very beautiful baby was born to the lady of a knight who was away in the Holy Land, and on his return he refused to accept it as his child, although she was born five months after his departure. He was so adamant and savage about it that he refused even to see her. Fearing lest he might do her some physical hurt, they placed the baby girl out to nurse, and in course of time she grew into lovely womanhood. On his return from the East many years later, he saw her and fell violently in love without knowing whom she really was. His lady having left him for a far better land during his absence abroad, and finding no obstacle to further matrimonial adventures, he made a violent and passionate set at her, and offered her his all if she would marry him. But her heart was already given to another worthy soldier of noble mien, and she told him that she was not free to marry anyone else.

'None shall have your virtue, but me!' he exclaimed, and her betrothed lover rode up at that moment just in time to protect her honour. She ran to him for protection, and her father raised his cross-bow. The arrow that was intended for his rival found its billet in her breast, and she sank in her lover's arms, pure and undefiled. The young soldier thereupon challenged him to fight, and told him whom he had killed. The knight fell on his knees beside his dead child, and then later went back to Palestine, assigning all his property to this gallant young soldier for his praiseworthy act. He never returned, and ever since the fair ladye Edythe appears at a certain time every year, floating on the lake, her eyes closed in sleep.

The other native, 'Willum' Storer, gave me much the same history, except that the girl tried to escape from her father with her lover in a boat, and that the arrow from his cross-bow sank the boat and the two sweethearts were drowned in the Broad.

Somehow this is a much more suitable ending and more in keeping with the apparition manifesting itself in the water.

'But', he added, 'you see 'er in th' mornin', early, just at sunrise, she leaves the water then, and you see 'er in the mist over the lake.'

It so happened that whilst the *Whitelady* lay in Barton Broad on

49

5 August 1930, my chance came to put the second story to the test.

Sleeping as we do, on deck, in the summer months, we were awakened by the water-fowl before the sun was actually up. It was quite light and the early dawn was fresh and had a 'nip' in it. A faint haze hung over the water and all around was still, and presently we saw quite distinctly the face of a beautiful girl reflected in the mist, and as we gazed spellbound at this lovely being, she opened her eyes and her face melted into a sweet smile, and then slowly faded away.

We were amazed. Never had we seen anything so wondrously perfect. It was too perfect to be human. It was as though some beautiful angel had peeped at us from heaven. Not one, but all four of us saw it, so it was no hallucination, either individual or collective.

Determined to see the vision again, if possible, we decided to wait until the following morning, and filled in the time by fishing, and a spot of sailing in the *Storm-pot*, the *Whitelady*'s tender. But alas, we were doomed to disappointment, for the next morning it blew quite hard, there was no mist and no beautiful Edythe.

Who would believe all this without seeing it? I for one would not, but I do advise those who are sufficiently interested to visit Barton Broad on 4 August and stay overnight and see it. You must take your chance of the weather which is never to be relied on, but it is well worth trying.

Evidently it was well known many years ago, for no less a person than Bishop Wentworth, in 1781, must have witnessed it, as he makes mention of it in his *Booke of Country Pastorals*, and there is no question that this beauteous young lady was so attractive and alluring in her loveliness that she stimulated his appeal to the Muse. A copy of his poem, *Barton Broad*, I have included here, to show that even Bishops can be susceptible to feminine charms, and can still fall for a lovely girl, even though they may be well past the first bloom of their halcyon youth.

> Oh, lovely waters of Elysia,
> Where dwell th' enchanted beings of a bye-gone world,
> And Hebe offers to her liege the
> Cup of nectar drained from the skies.
> Zeus in all his majesty ne'er knew
> Such ecstasy as thy sweet spirit brings.
> Oh, angel of this peaceful mere,
> Evoking dreams of pure serenest calm,
> Soothing those tired fragments of the mind,
> And blessing with thy subtle fragrance
> The souls of man who seek thy peace
> Of gentlest tranquility and rest.
> Oh, lady of enchantment, who asleep,
> Reposing in the mirror of this lake,
> I come to ask of thee thy love,
> For thou indeed art loveliness itself.
> Thy beauteous face upturned in silent speech,
> With closed eyes, still floats serenely on.
> What mortal can thy mystic secret guess,
> And why those gentle orbs are closed
> In sleep the livelong hour?
> At dewy morn thy figure of envisaged
> Beauty, casts its spell upon
> The morning mist, ere Aurora has
> Across the morning sky
> Swept in her chariot from the chase
> With Diana, and Apollo for thy guide.
> What spell dost work upon the clay
> Of mortal fashioning, and what response,
> As from the matin's mist thy face
> Reveals thine open orbs and sends
> Sweet peace, beyond all peace
> As ever known to men?
> – Wentworth (From *Booke of Country Pastorals*, 1781)

Potter Heigham

Like many other places in these Western Isles of Europe, this name has puzzled a good many inquisitive people, myself included, but 'Potter', as it is affectionately known by the countless thousands who visit it annually, is a place to itself, does not attempt to vie with any of its compeers in Broadland, and is quite satisfied if those who come and go carry away with them happy memories of their stay, the amenities it affords as a meeting ground for all Broads lovers, the sport it has to offer, and the number of pretty girls who add lustre to the gaiety and attraction of the higher reaches of the Thurne. It can also boast of a 'spot' of good fishing to those whose inclinations favour the rod and reel, whilst one matter it has just reason to be proud of is its – 'ghost'.

Ha-ha, a real succulent ghost story, and one to make your blood go all gu-ey, and your spinal-cord flutter like a flag in a high wind.

I haven't seen it yet, but it is my intention to do so this year (D.V., and W.P. or not) by hook or by crook, and on 31 May, this year of grace, 1931, my boat will be alongside the bank, at a safe distance from the bridge, and as the church-clock strikes the midnight hour, every effort will be made to 'shoot' the episode, which for so many decades has thrilled the listener and sent its eye-witnesses bald.

Two men at Potter have seen it within recent years, and one's hair went snow-white, whilst the other man's fell off in the night. George Hallness saw it in 1926, and Matthew Denham as late as last year, 1930.

Don't listen to the natives who pooh-pooh the story. They're afraid that it may scare people away and would be bad for business, but they forget that the blessed and bright young things of this generation are not one whit afraid of the supernatural, and even the most timid of girls, who would scream at the sight of a harmless little mouse or beetle, will go miles and miles and suffer no end of inconvenience to witness a super-normal manifestation, and the more grim and deathly it may happen to be the greater its attraction.

John Fraser, my friend who saw it last year, is a hard-grained bra'

Hielander with no nonsense about him, and he's coming with me next May to help photograph it.

Some say that to witness these phenomena is to court disaster, if not at the time, perhaps later on, but don't you believe it. No metaphysical visions have yet caused harm to mortal man, and if they really have this power, then I ought to have found my misereri mei thirty years ago. Anyway, we are looking forward with great zest to 31 May next, and with luck I hope to see you there.

Now for the story. Let Fraser tell it. Come on, John!

'All right. Anything for peace.'

In the year 1741 there lived at the big manor called Bastwick Place – which is short for 'palace', because it was once an episcopal residence of My Lord Bishop of Norwiche – a very fine man, who was regarded as the most beautiful at Court. Sir Godfrey Haslitt was not only very goodly to look upon, but was very well endowed with this world's goods, and money to him was a Tennysonian book. His father, the fifth baronet of the line, had amassed a huge fortune out East, and turned up his toes before he had time to enjoy it, leaving an already motherless son of twenty-eight to fend for himself in a cruel world with nothing at his back but the title, this large fortune, the moiety of the manor, a university education, a passion for horses, and a cordial dislike for women. The last mentioned quality only served to whet the appetites of the fine ladies at Court, and to prompt them to vie with each other in arranging which of their daughters he should lead to the altar. But to everybody's chagrin he appeared to be proof against the overwhelming charm of each eligible young girl who was placed in his path, and many a disconsolate maiden went to bed and sobbed her little heart out for very love of him, and fell asleep on a tear-soaked pillow to dream of a future that was not for her. Ah me, lackaday!

One day at Windsor the King himself took him up to a very lovely girl at the Court ball, and handed him over to her for a partner. His Majesty had come to hear of his indifference for the fair sex, and so singled out the most beautiful demoiselle present, hoping for the best, and praying that it would come off.

Sir Godfrey was the essence of politeness, and whilst feeling he had been greatly honoured, yet kept a tight curb on himself for fear he might fall a victim to her surpassing beauty. The Lady Evelyn's mother was frightfully bucked, and preened herself like a peacock for the rest of the evening, bubbling over with the reflected glory of this great honour.

In less than an hour it was common property at the Court that Evelyn Lady Montefiore Carew was betrothed, and that she had actually snaffled this rara avis, and that in due course the official notice of their betrothal would be announced. Now the truth of the matter was this. Sir Godfrey received his partner at the hands of his monarch, and gazing down upon her from his great height, not from any sense of overwhelming superiority, but more in a protective sense, lest he might be led into some kind of matrimonial 'decoy', could not help noticing that the eyes of the entire assembly were upon him and were filled with wonder as to how he was going to treat her.

His partner was so perfectly feminine and desirable, on account of her ravishing beauty and gentle loveliness, that it was fervently hoped that he would not turn a blind eye upon this iridescent gem of femininity and lustrous specimen of radiant girlhood.

Her mother, a shrewd woman forsooth, was very careful not to attempt to precipitate matters, but in the presence of King George at the supper table invited this very desirable and hoped-for son-in-law to stay with them at Castle Lynn for the hunting, and the King himself butted in and said:

'Yes, you must come. I'm coming – am I not, Lady Carew – and I should like to meet you there.'

'Sir,' replied Sir Godfrey, 'if it be your royal desire, nothing could make me happier than to accept this kind invitation.'

In due course the great day arrived, and Castle Lynn became a seething formicarium of excitement, because of the royal visit and the hunting. It was the first time in all history that a real live monarch had ever been in or near the neighbourhood, and consequently there was great rejoicing amongst the local populace concerning the 'doings up at the Manor'. Everybody in the village was busy and up to their eyes in work, each contributing his or her quota of energy towards making things 'go', but the greatest speculation prevailed concerning the Lady Evelyn, and most people were certain that she was going to fall for the King himself.

Now Lady Carew was dead set on making Sir Godfrey her son-in-law, and with that determination in mind, she took her daughter aside and carefully instructed her as to what she should and should not do, and, in addition, two weeks prior to the opening of the hunting season, they journeyed together to the distant village of Belaugh, where resided an old witch, who made love philtres.

During the process of mixing the philtre, the Lady Evelyn had to stand in the centre of a circle on the floor, and swear that whatever price was demanded for the success of the magic spell, it should be paid, and her doting mother promised, as guarantor, that she would accept the penalty herself if payment was not made. The old fool promised everything she was asked, and after the powder was made

54

she swore her own soul and her daughter's away without realising what she had done. There was a flash of flame, the floor opened up and the flame withdrew into the ground, leaving a nasty and acrid smell of brimstone in their nostrils. They were both very frightened, and the young girl came over very ill, but she recovered on gaining the air, and both mother and daughter were very glad when they were once more on their homeward journey.

When the house filled up for the hunting, Sir Godfrey was received with every possible display of welcome, and on the very night of his arrival the philtre was surreptitiously slipped into his hot punch.

That night he dreamed of women as he had never thought of them before, and within two days he was trailing around after the Lady Evelyn like a tame tiger.

The change which had come over him almost blinded him to everything else, and it was so noticeable that it did not take long for gossip to run high and conviction even higher. His embittered dislike for the fair sex had been completely metamorphosed into an irresistible desire to be with them, and all his callous indifferences to their charm was now sublimated in an intense devotion to the beautiful and lovely daughter of the house.

At the end of a week he was unable to contain himself any longer, and approaching her old father and doting and cunning old mother, he asked permission, as a gentleman should, to pay court to their daughter. Their consent being granted with just enough hesitation to stimulate further his desire to make her his own, he went flat out to win her. Report had it that she coyly refused him twice, but being a man who would not take 'No' for an answer for anything he had once set his mind on doing, or possessing, he stuck to his programme, and the third time he asked, she wilted on his shoulder, dried her tearless eyes upon a little lace hanky, and turning her pale little face up to his, their pact was sealed in a rapturous embrace. He placed a half-hoop circlet on her finger, and the next morning at luncheon informed his host and hostess of his colossal success, and the official announcement of their betrothal was made there and then. The news spread like a prairie-fire, and within two days it was publicly announced in London.

The engagement lasted for some months, and on 31 May of the following year, 1741, they were married by special licence in Norwiche Cathedral by the Lord Abbot of St Benet's-at-Holm and Norwiche – which fact, by the way is rather interesting in that my Lord Bishop of Norwich today is the only ecclesiastic of the established church who still holds the title of a dignitary in the Roman communion.

A great feast was prepared in the cathedral city, and later in the afternoon a large bridal procession of coaches and horses over a mile

55

long wended its way back to Bastwick Place, where the nuptials were to receive the episcopal benediction. The entire concourse were gathered together in the huge hall awaiting the arrival of the bishop, who had been delayed by one of his wheelers going lame. Ten o'clock struck, and everybody was getting very anxious; eleven o'clock struck, and still he failed to arrive.

On the stroke of midnight, the outer gates were flung open and the bishop's coach arrived with his lordship robed in mitre and cope with his suite in all their regalia. The large front doors to the hall were rolled back, the bishop mounted the steps, and then suddenly rushed madly into the midst of the assembly, followed by his satellites.

Such undignified behaviour in one of such exalted rank, and clad with the ecclesiastical vestments pertaining to his dignity, was more than a shock in itself for everybody, but when as suddenly he and his attendants changed to skeletons, the entire gathering just fell back and collapsed. Seizing the beautiful bride, he raised her kicking and screaming, in his arms, and raced out of the hall with her, leaving behind a dense cloud of sulphurous smoke, and jumping on to the box of the coach, he held on to his fainting burden with one arm whilst with the other hand he grabbed the ribbons, and shouting at the horses, they swung out of the drive-gates and raced away down the road, the leaders and wheelers galloping for all they were worth, and streaks of fire flashing from their nostrils as they tore along towards Heigham Bridge. The few people who happened to be about saw a luminous coach dash past, its wheels glowing with phosphorescence, and driven madly by a skeleton who appeared to be on fire inside, and clothed in the canonicals of a bishop with his mitre all cock-eye, and its bands fluttering in the wind behind him. The coach swayed from side to side in its mad career, and streams of sparks flew from the wheels as they came along the road.

At last, as it came to the bridge, it swayed so violently that it struck the stone-work, and on reaching the centre the whole coach was smashed into a thousand flaming pieces, and was flung with its contents, horses and all, over the parapet into the Thurne beneath. There was a terrific roar, a fountain of flame shot up, and it was all over. Away down the road just beyond Bastwick there was a red flickering glow in the sky, which told of the fate of the great house and of nearly everyone who was in it. The fair Lady Evelyn had paid the price she promised.

Although the grand denouement takes place at Heigham Bridge, it is known as the ghost of Potter Heigham, but in my opinion it should be called the spectre of Bastwick.

When I saw it last year, two others were with me, and we were all basking on deck moon-bathing – you cannot sleep in the cabin on fine warm nights – and we were sitting up in our pyjamas smoking a final pipe before turning in, when, a moment after midnight had struck, we heard a yelling and a shouting coming closer and closer, and getting louder as it came. We looked hard at each other, and then hopped off on to the bank to try and locate it.

There, coming down that long open road across the flat country, which lies between the bridge and the village of Bastwick was a four-in-hand driven by a maniac coachman. Swaying from side to side behind four equally mad black horses, which were racing at a furious gallop, the coach was leaving a stream of sparks in the wake of each wheel. The body of the vehicle seemed to be on fire within and without. Skeletons crowded on top and inside, and the driver, wearing a bishop's cope which falling back displayed his skeleton body, his mitre all awry and tipped half over his grinning skull, had his arm around a fainting girl in bridal array, and was holding the reins in his right, bony fist.

Approaching the bridge at a break-neck speed, they struck the stone-work with an ear-splitting crash, the coach was smashed to pieces, and the horses, people and blazing fragments were flung high into the air and fell, a tangled, tumbling mass, into the river below. A huge flame shot up from the water as the splash took place and was followed by a most sinister silence, that made our backs go icy-cold, and froze the very blood in our veins.

It was the silence of Death.

South Walsham

'Do you mean to say you never heard of our "ghost" who comes here regularly every First of May?' My informant leaned back and eyed me very critically.

'Do you mean to tell me? Well!' he went on, putting his tankard on the counter with definite precision and calculated to draw attention to its need for replenishment. 'Why, hang it, sir, we've the finest "ghost" in all Norfolk here on South Walsham Broad. Norfolk's full of them, I know, and so's Suffolk, come to that, but there isn't one of them can look at ours. Yes, sir, I know what you're going to say, or rather what you're thinking. Every mother's chickens are swans, but it isn't necessary in this case. People come from far and near to see it, and on the evening of the First of May you'll often find the Broad lined with boats, and little crowds of people on the banks where they can see. Lots of them go away disappointed, because it isn't for all of us to see the things which are supernatural. Some can and some can't. You and I, for instance, might both be able to see spirits and things like that, but not necessarily the same ones. They say it is a question of sensitiveness to light vibrations in the eyes that decides as to whether or not you can perceive these manifestations. Or again, you might be able to see them today, and not tomorrow or some other time, because your faculty of perception varies from one moment to the next. Funny creatures, aren't we? Oh, well – thanks very much, that's very nice of you, I'll have a little mild ale if I may. Very kind, I'm sure.'

The man, who was evidently a well-informed person, spoke with excellent diction, and had the verbal delivery and demeanour of a Cantab. I was also taken with the idea that I had here found a mine of information and a source of possible help. He turned out to be a hind on a large estate, a job which he had taken up for its open-air amenities, as he had developed a weak spot in his left lung whilst at Caius. He had had to relinquish his training for the law and get back to Nature, a counsel upon which he had very wisely acted.

'Yes,' he continued, evidently glad to have someone to talk to, 'some fellows come down every year for the First of May and get back the following day. Last year it was remarkably good. Let's sit down and I'll tell you about it, and then perhaps you might like to join our little party this year.'

I said I would very much, and I did, and was more than repaid for my trouble. That was three years ago, but I'll first give you his account, and then my own of what actually happened when I had the good fortune to be present.

'You are aware,' he explained, 'that the Vikings and their hordes were a continual source of anxiety to the British people long before the Romans came, and even during the Roman occupation, but the moment they left these shores, which they did early in the fifth century, these raiders came over and gave no end of trouble. They were a pagan race and were resented exceedingly by the Britishers, who never hesitated to fight them when they could and strive to their utmost to drive them out.

'One famous Viking, Oscar, the son of Saturn, priest-king and sailor, the well-beloved of the gods, and famed throughout all Western Europe as the greatest of all tyrants, landed on the shores of Norfolk close to Cromer, and proclaimed it part of his kingdom. He sailed around the coast and entered the River Bure and sacked and pillaged every homestead on his way. It was at South Walsham he made his headquarters and met his nemesis. It is said that a small girl of ten from the village was sent to find some mushrooms for him, and that her mother had a say in it and saw to it that the 'right' ones were procured.

'The result was a viking's funeral, and every First of May, as the hour of midnight strikes, the Broad becomes filled with boats, the viking's ship is brought out into the middle of the lake, faggots are piled high on board, and lighted. The body of the son of Saturn is cremated, the ship burns to the water-line and then disappears.'

That is, roughly, what my friend told me, and it was just sufficient to whet my appetite and desire to witness this extraordinary apparition, so accordingly I went down to South Walsham Broad last year with four others, chartered a cruiser, and on the evening of the First of May we were snugly moored down on the south-eastern shore, well out of the way, yet having an excellent view of the entire water.

We had finished supper and 'washed up', like good yachtsmen always do before taking their leisure, and were out on deck basking in the starlight, because there was no moon, and the smoke was wreathing itself up from our pipes undisturbed, the long grey streamers rising up like the smoke from chimneys on a dead calm day, and which causes the old West of England housewife to remark: 'Annuther vine day-y, to be sure!'

It was a perfect night. The stars shone and twinkled with such clearness that they appeared ever so much lower down than is their usual wont. The water-fowl had departed for the night, whilst the little moorhen and dabchicks had finished their daily round of scrounging for food, and after their hard day's work had packed up and turned in. The crested grebe, satisfied with his labours of the preceding twelve hours, had roosted 'mongst the reeds, and closed his eyes in peaceful anticipation of the morrow. London, work and hustle were at the moment unknown quantities, and nothing more remote could have disturbed our sacred peace, which was so complete and absorbing that even the striking of a match to light one's pipe seemed all but a crime, so still was everything around.

We were lying quite quietly and enjoying the placidity of our environment, when suddenly the little ship was rudely shaken by a bump as of some heavy vessel colliding with us. We sprang up and heard some people talking, but could see nobody, although there was sufficient light to outline any object near and around us. We looked over the side and all around, but without success. We could see nothing, absolutely nothing. The boat, or whatever it was, with its complement pushed past us, rubbing our sides as it went, and the people aboard it still talking, but in a language we could not understand. It was most weird to follow them by their sound and yet be quite unable to see them. Jefferson looked at me bewildered, and the look went round. Things were looking up. Conditions were verging on the uncanny, when as suddenly as before, and without any warning, the vessel rocked, and rocked again, and again and again; the sound of voices in an unknown tongue were all about us, on the deck, in the saloon and the cockpit. It was as though we had been boarded by a gang of invisibles. We got up and searched the ship, but we were quite by ourselves, and yet the voices around us kept passing and re-passing us. Our metaphysical visitors were evidently quite at home, and seemed to pass right through us as they walked about; in short, they could no more see us than we could see them.

Another question which rose in our minds was whether their vessel had merged into ours, or were they tied up alongside of us and their occupants come aboard. As they, too, had come to the Broad, matter must have, up to a point, been visible to them, or else they would not have known where they were, and therefore it is reasonable to assume that they could see and feel our boat, if they could not actually see us.

Another bump shook the whole vessel badly, and from the conversation between the people already on board and their friends who had evidently just arrived, it appeared – sounds silly to say 'appeared', doesn't it, when we couldn't see anything? – nevertheless, it appeared from their tones that they also were surprised at something unusual and perhaps could hear us talking but could not see us. We tried all manner of divers means to check our conclusions, waiting for a lull in their converse and then speaking loudly to each other. As we did so, their conversation stopped as though they were listening, and the moment we ceased they broke out afresh and gabbled at each other as though they were checking their suppositions also.

Some people would, quite reasonably, have been seized with alarm at such a happening. Somehow we were not the least bit affrighted, but on the contrary we became deeply interested. It was all to absorbing to feel anything in the nature of apprehension about it, and we kept this up for quite a while.

The next thing we heard was a hail from them to some invisible friends who evidently were passing at some little distance away. Back came the response from the others, and then we heard a horn. It was a call on a brass instrument and was definitely blown. We peered out into the semi-darkness, but could see nothing. Then our boat as definitely rocked again as though our visitors were moving about. There was no mistake about this, because these Broads cruisers are so light that the slightest movement on board becomes self-evident immediately, and at one moment, when we were perfectly quiet and still, the boat careened over so suddenly that we had to seize hold of the nearest fixture within reach to save ourselves being slid off the deck into the water. It then as quickly righted itself. We could not decide if they were actually on our little ship, or whether theirs had merged into ours and they were still aboard their own within ours.

All this sounds very complicated and possibly far-fetched, but if these things had not really happened, it is highly improbable that you would be reading this description of them, and if these actual details appear to be somewhat lacking in conviction, it is to be prayed you will not measure their insufficiency by their presentation, for no words can faithfully portray the emotions which conflicted us, and make this happening so difficult to record. If I tell you our flesh fairly 'crept', I should only be repeating the jargon vernacular so familiar with the retailer of 'spook-stuff'. Sematics of our finite variety must of necessity fail sadly in the conveyance of meanings, emotions, and the abstract in general. The most that we can do is to impart, in the limited phraseology at our disposal, the information which is ours to give, in spite of an all too insufficient vocabulary. This is always the drawback of a phonetic language as against the idiogramatics of, say, the Chinese, who have no alphabet at all, but three thousand symbols to play about with instead.

It is difficult to imagine anything more uncomfortable than the invisible presence of people round and about one, not only walking and moving about, but right through you. There was something, too, about their speech which was intensely weird. It was always on the other side of an invisible curtain, though perfectly distinct and clear. Sometimes the voices came from here, then there, and the next time, as it were, from within one's very own self, when one hadn't made a sound.

One cannot help thinking of the colossal sums of money spent by the craving credulous in seeking communication with the spirit-world, or even experiencing convincing proof of the existence of the metaphysical. Large gatherings flock to assembly halls to listen to mere tyros of only a few years' experience holding forth as leaders, and who know all about the 'hereafter', when a moment's experience of the 'other side' and its manifestations in Norfolk and Suffolk would provide enough convincing testimony for all in ten minutes. If ever proof of a fourth dimension was needed, here it is, and in plenty, and one thing which does impress itself upon those who are scientifically inclined and interested is the stupidity of trying to measure or control these unseen agencies by three dimensional means. No science of the physical order is capable of dealing with those things which are outside the realm of our finite processes.

But what a digression. We were talking about the Broad at South Walsham. I know your interest is as deep as mine, therefore you should not encourage me, otherwise divergence is unavoidable. So let's on!

Then other boats apparently arrived in their scores, and from what it was possible to gauge by their sounds, lined the Broad from end to end. We had by now become so accustomed to our extraordinary situation that the novelty of it did not strike us as unusual. We no longer felt the intense concern for our safety that first filled us with apprehension.

MacDowell's suggestion that we should offer spirits to the spirits met with little response, especially as the whisky was fairly low and the gin had not yet been opened.

Whatever was taking place beyond the veil was evidently of great interest to our visitors, and that they had foregathered for some great event there could be no question. Was it possible that they were there for the self-same purpose as ourselves? The chances were in favour of it anyway, and if this was the case, these metaphysical entities were of the Viking period, and spoke their Nordic tongue, which sufficiently will explain our inability to comprehend a single word of their noisy chatterings. How many were there it is impossible to estimate, as the Broad seemed to be full of them.

We were still alternating our conversation with theirs, when suddenly a deathly silence fell upon the entire water, and you could have heard a rain-drop fall. Then from the direction of the entrance to the Broad came the roll of muffled drums. Nearer and nearer they came, and close behind them followed a ship which we were quite able to descry against the darkness beyond.

It was a typical Viking's vessel with its mast and sail and many oars. Slowly it came down the Broad, becoming clearer as it approached, and we could now make it out quite clearly. Stacked up on the deck of this ship was a mass of faggots tied together in huge bundles, and reaching nearly to the top of the mast. Surmounting this was something which was covered by a large cloth that hung down all around. Presently the ship hove to, and a fanfare of horns was blown which resounded in all directions and echoed back. Then we saw several smaller boats appear out of the darkness, approach the 'piled-high' vessel, take off the rowers, and pulling away from the ship, they slowly vanished into the darkness around.

We now noticed a light appear in the centre of the stack of faggots on the ship, and soon clouds of dense black smoke wreathed upwards towards the stars. In a few moments long flames began to appear, then disappear, and after a short while, the whole mass was a roaring, blazing furnace, and the tall flames were licking up a hundred feet high. It roared and crackled and spit and fumed, as though it were seething with anger. No other sound could be heard but this blazing, merciless pyre. Sparks shot up in dense masses of hysterical pyrotechny. The flames seemed to lash the very heavens, and the noise of their waving folds sounded like huge flags slapping in a high wind. Spitting and spurting in every direction, this marvellous conflagration consumed everything on board the vessel, the interior of which had become a roaring hell, belching forth myriads of scintillating meteors which fell in golden showers from a great height into the waters around.

The vessel itself was now a blazing mass, and the heat was intense. We could easily feel it, though we were so far away. Rumbling and howling, this infuriated inferno slowly settled itself down, and its light, which was sufficient to illuminate the whole country for miles around, gradually softened, the whip-like tongues of amber fire became less and less, until presently there was nothing left but a glowing red hull, like some Plutonic vessel bound for a distant shore in the realms of Sheol.

Just then the moon began to rise, and as Luna rose from her couch and bathed the sleeping world in her pale and gentle rays, the dense black cloud of smoke could be seen curling away like some huge inky black serpent across the fleckless nocturnal sky, and the surrounding reeds and trees slowly became more visible, the large Viking's ship, glowing like a mass of incandescent coke in a gas retort, gradually sank beneath the waters and faded out of being.

Horning

When one glides along the river that washes the banks of lovely Horning, or saunters carelessly down the village street, it is difficult to imagine that this delicious and desirable little townlet could ever be associated with the super-normal, and yet its very atmosphere, to those who are sensitive, is just throbbing with everything that is psychic.

There is nothing sinister at Horning, and therefore the phenomena which take place annually in this snug little place only serve to add to its allurement. What is it that makes Horning so attractive? That it certainly is so is borne out by the fact that few people can pass it by unheeded. The very air is electrically alive with something which few people can ignore, and yet if you were to ask them what it was that attracted them, you would immediately get them guessing. There is a significance, inexplicable and elusive, which not only draws, but holds one to it, and never so marked is this as when one prepares to leave it. This subtle influence is begotten of tradition, that great realm of an unwritten past which is more reliable than all the written records of accepted history. History can vary according to the historian, but tradition never dies. It may be augmented, it may even suffer detraction, but fundamentally it carries down in the blood of the people, in the very marrow of their hereditary memories, ready to burgeon into fact when occasion arises and opportunity affords. And this is what catches the fancy of the visitor's mind, and unbeknown to him makes its conditions attractive by the breath of unspoken memory vibrating with sympathetic desire for expression. It is as though the past endeavours to reveal itself by striking those chords of harmony in the subconscious mind which, often uninterpretable to the materialist, leaves him with a 'call', which he may not understand, to come again.

Horning, whose name was once Horningham, and before that Horlingham, and earlier still Hurlingham, most certainly has a 'call', just as have the desert and the sea. Once you have been there, you have to go back, even though you may be at the other end of the world. Something starts a series of events which in the beginning are

quite unassociated with the objective, and yet each one bears upon the next, until sooner or later you find yourself on your way back to visit it once more.

This beautiful oasis dates back to the time of Elle and Cissa, and I should imagine that Cissa must have been very disappointed on visiting Elle, that he had not landed in the country of the North-folk himself, and let Elle go around to Regnum in the south.

I was in the lounge of the 'Swan' one evening after dinner when

I got into conversation with a very well-informed man, and happened to remark that it was a pity Elle couldn't see it as it is today, or that we couldn't look back and see it as it used to be. He took his pipe out of his mouth and looked at me very hard.

'Somebody been talking?' he enquired.

I assured him that no one had as yet said anything at all to me which was very definite, but enough to set me thinking, and that——

He interrupted my reply and tapping out his ash, remarked: 'If you really are interested in traditional and historical legend I'll tell you the story of Horning, and an interesting one it is. At least, I think so. I don't know if Horning is mentioned in Domesday, because its greater interest to my mind goes back a good six hundred years before then, when the Romans evacuated Britain, and left the people to fend for themselves against the Saxons and the Danes, whilst Branudonum, the modern Brancaster, ceased to be one of the fortresses of the chain which was built from the Wash to Porchester by Marcus Carausius, who was not only Count of the Saxon Shore, as this stretch of coast was called, but who became Emperor of the Roman Empire in the West. It was he, you know, who founded the Royal Mint in London, and in the British Museum you can see some of his coins.

'As soon as the Romans had gone, in AD 410, the country was overrun by Saxons, Danes, Jutes and Norsemen, and they fought like wolves over their "finds", until eventually the Saxons drove the Danes out, and those that were left behind had to submit to Saxon rule or go under. Up to the coming of Elle and his host, Caistor-by-Norwich, which was known as Venta Icenorum, was the nearest town of any importance to Horning, whilst this little place had been scarcely interfered with, and the Britons still lived in their little wattle houses and tilled the land. But the Saxon eye for beauty could not allow it to remain any longer in this primitive state, and so they practically rebuilt it, replacing the old wattling with good solid cement and flint. When it was completed, and a wide village street had now superseded the collection of old and scattered huts, a Christian church was built, and King Elle – or Ella – visited it with all the full state ceremonial, becoming an East Anglian Monarch.

'When it was announced that the King himself was coming to Horning, the village busied itself and prepared for this great honour. The street was gay with banners, flags and banderols, whilst a triumphal arch, constructed out of branches of trees cut for the purpose, was erected at each end of it. Everybody put on his best array, shops were closed and the entire locality gave itself up to holiday and rejoicing.

'In the distance the sound of drums was heard, and presently the King himself arrived in a procession of archers, halberdiers, and gentlemen-at-arms, followed by a never-ending column of soldiers, mounted and foot. The King was seated on a white charger, which walked with stately mien between two royal grooms who held its bridle by two golden straps.

'As the East Anglian Monarch entered one end of the village, another procession was entering at the other, and this was the Lord Abbot of Norwiche and St Benedict's-at-Holm, who had come to meet and welcome him. The mitred abbot arrived in his own state-coach, wearing his cope, mitre, and pectoral cross, and carried his crozier. The meeting between these two powers of Church and State was a very inspiring spectacle and their mutual interchange of greetings were most cordial. They received each other as only two such great dignitaries of the realm could, and the scene on the grass sward between the village roadway and the river – there were no houses on the river side of the street in those days – bore witness to the deepest amity and respect they each held for the other's rank.

'The King dismounted and kneeling on the bare grass removed his crown and received the episcopal benediction. The Lord Abbot then took the golden circlet from the hands of Elle, and replacing it on the Monarch's head, exclaimed:

'"Thou hast come to save and protect a worthy people. Thou art indeed well-called 'Elle' – the Swan. Thou art the Swan of Peace."

'And from that time there has always been a "Swan" at Horning.

'It is commonly known that the ancient custom of nicknames, which originally came over with the Saxons, Norsemen and Danes, still persists amongst the people, who attach to each other sobriquets peculiar to some characteristic of the person concerned, and by which, in many cases, they are better known than by their Christian or baptismal appellations. "Pudden-face" Adams, and "Boss-eye" Gibson, "Dirt" Fletcher, and "Cat" Barnes will greet each other and take no offence at all.

'And so the "Swan" of the North-folk came and ruled a splendid people, and travelled all over his kingdom of East Anglia, visiting those of his subjects who might otherwise have never seen their King.

'At Reedham he built a palace and established his High Court of Justice there. At Caistor – or Castor, or Castra – he built another palace, and at Beccles a magnificent church, and founded a very large monastery at Holy Cross.

'But it is this great scene of their first meeting which makes Horning singularly unique. Now, you know as well as I do that certain places become impressed by great occasions and happenings, and that one often hears a sensitive person say. "I don't like that house," or "I can't stay in that room," although they cannot explain why, but on investigation it is often found that something tragic has happened in that place and left its impressions, as it were, in the atmosphere or walls, and to certain temperaments these most certainly make themselves felt.

'It must not be imagined that only bad or evil influences possess the prerogative of continuity. On the contrary, everything that is emotional leaves its impress, and the more intense the emotion, whether good, bad or indifferent, the greater its power of persistence. And so that is how it comes about that once every five years – I do not know why it should be five, but five it is – the most wonderful transformation scene takes place in this delightful little township.

'On 21 July every five years, with the precision of clockwork, as soon as it is dark, quite dark, all the buildings on the riverside disappear. Petrol pumps, boat-sheds, jetties, inns and houses, everything between the river and the roadway completely vanishes, leaving a beautiful grass lawn the whole length of the village, whilst the houses on the far side of the street entirely change their shape and appearance and again become Saxon in style and character. Shrines with lighted tapers appear in the windows, flags bedeck the whole street, and at each end of the village there appears a triumphal arch of evergreen. Then the whole scene takes place as I have already described to you and all the ceremonial is re-enacted, and the Lord Abbot of St Benet's-at-Holm places the crown on Elle's head, and bestows his sacred benisons upon the entire assembly. The processions re-form and pass out of the village in the direction of St Benet's, the tapers slowly go out, the solitude returns once more, and the houses come back, the jetties and boat-slips and everything resumes its appearance as you know it today.

'One interesting point in this spectacular phenomenon is that with all this huge concourse of people who throw themselves into wild abandon and rejoicing, not a sound is heard the whole time. The sound vibrations appear to have spent themselves in the course of fifteen hundred years, but the emotional undulations in the ether seem to have persisted without any sense of diminution. When is it expected again, did you say? Well, as near as I can make out – let me see, thirty, twenty-nine, eight, seven, six – yes, six and five's eleven. That's it. This year, 1931. Are you sensitive, or psychic, or anything like that? Well, if you are, you will see this most wonderful happening, and I can assure you, it is the most striking thing I've ever witnessed in my life. Yes, I've seen it, and I could introduce several to you who've seen it as well. Although it is not too much talked about, you'd be surprised at the number of visitors who flock here from all parts on 21 July every year, on the off-chance of being present at this strange occurrence, in spite of the fact that actually it only takes place once in every five years. Still, it's the thrill of the possibility, the attraction of the elusive that draws them, and anything with a spice of romance or the super-normal in it always draws the crowd. Of course, it's good for business, mind you, and the tradespeople welcome this special influx, and no one here is ever scared or frightened about the phenomenon.

'Many people come and see nothing, even on the correct date, but then you do not need me to tell you that all people are not alike in their powers of receiving vibrations. We cannot see the sun's rays, for instance, but only those things which they fall on and so light up.

'Again, our eyes vary considerably in what they can enable us to see, some are more sensitive to certain light rays or vibrations than others. As an instance, take the vibrational emanations of light which our own living bodies emit and are commonly known as the "aurae", so beloved of seers and necromancers, fortune-tellers and the like, who try to impose on the credulous that they have special powers of seeing your spiritual lights. Well, thanks to the great Dr Kilner, of St Thomas's Hospital, his investigations clearly proved that anyone could see an "aura" if they wished, and that if their retinæ were not equal to recording the radio-active emanations referred to, they could be made so by use of his double cyanide screen.

'And further, all ears are not capable of appreciating the same sounds, and heaps of people are what is termed "note-deaf", in that they are unable to hear certain notes, whilst the rest of the gamut may be perfectly clear and defined. So is it with psychic phenomena. Some are not sensitive to certain vibrations, whilst others are acutely so. This explains why some people can see "ghosts", and others are absolutely incapable of doing so, and it is those in the last category who invariably deny even the possibility of such manifestations. All this is perhaps irrelevant, but nevertheless to my way of thinking of great interest.

'Now, to come back to Horning. If you intend coming along this year to try and witness this gorgeous episode, you must get here about six in the evening. Don't, on any account, have anything to eat or drink after eight o'clock until the affair is over, and specially let me warn you not to touch any strong liquor that night. Give it a complete miss, because the ingestion of alcohol, however slight, does certainly excite your nerves and throw out of gear your receptivity of what you might otherwise see. Bring with you warm wraps and coats, and some good thick rugs, because just before this superb spectacle takes place, the temperature falls suddenly, and you are likely to take a bad chill, and nothing is worth that risk.

'The position I recommend you to take up is on the opposite side of the river about eighty to a hundred yards down-stream from the bend by the "Swan".

'One more suggestion I would like to make is that you prepare yourself for the better perception of this vision, by keeping ever so quiet from about ten p.m. onwards. This allows your nervous system to quieten down, and becoming rested, makes itself much more sensitive to reception than it otherwise would be.

'John Holmes, a great pal of mine, has witnessed this happening every five years since he was a boy, and prepares himself, as I have recommended you should, for a whole week beforehand.

'Some noisy, inconsiderate people, two appearances ago, who had heard of these "ombres Saxes", moored right alongside the jetty on the village side, and made such a row and kicked up such a drunken, guffawing hullabaloo whilst the scene was taking place, that they not only saw nothing themselves, but, in addition, seriously disturbed the vibrational conditions for everybody else, with the result that not all of the episode could materialise. What actually was able to, appeared to be seen through a curtain of haze, and was so dimmed that the major portion of the affair was quite lost.

'By the way, if you do intend to come this year, keep a look-out for the *Penguin*, and come alongside. We shall be on the other bank from here, so give us a hail, and come aboard. We'll be awfully glad to see you and we can compare notes. Here's your very best. Cheery-ho!'

Brundall

When Will'um Carbol looked me straight in the eyes and nodded his confirmation that dear little Brundall really could boast of a spectral visitation, I did not exactly laugh, but anything so remotely improbably as that was beyond the wildest dreams of even an imaginative mind like mine.

It is not difficult to imagine anything if you care to give your mind to it, but such a flight of fancy as this would have been to my way of thinking, wild indeed. But Norfolk is Norfolk, and if some of the natives in those parts still cling dearly to their cherished traditions, all the more praise to them, because in these days of unconventional and unbridled behaviour, it is good to see romance still holding its own at a time when mechanised conditions and science have swept sentiment aside against the wall, and pushed civilisation forward in its blind endeavour to capture the elusive.

Friend Carbol is a good sort and has hewn and delved in this beauty spot since he was a boy, and that's going back a long way. His long line of labouring ancestors had worked on the land in an unbroken record of honest industry, and so when Will'um imparted a serious piece of information such as this, it was not a matter for risible criticism, but rather something that was worthy of respectful acceptance, which, whether it was true or not, was a point that did not call for question and, on the contrary, commanded deep and sincere interest.

'Ayes, 'bor. We don't mind speakin' of it to the likes o' you, 'cause you be fair wholly reasonable, whilst some others do fairly make me shut up like a clam, 'bor, like a clam. And it's very kind o' you, 'bor, but you do fill up th' mug the third time. My best respects. It's a long story, 'bor. What I means is, it do go back a long way, aye, before Norwich had a cathedral at all.

'The Lord Abbot o' St Benet's looked after the parish in them days, as he do now, except that he's Bishop o' Norwich as well. And we are fair wholly fond of him, too. But the Lord Bishop I do go to tell you about, was a great riverman, and he did use to have his own barge in which he went to the different parts of his parish when he

72

could. His coach used to go around by road and pick him up where necessary, but as far as he could, he always used the water, and I don't blame him neither 'cause he was a good man and evil spirits don't like the river. Won't come near it if they can help it. Don't ask me why, 'bor, 'cause I don't know, nor nobody else neither, that I'm sartin.

'As I was a sayin', me Lord Abbot was a fine feller, a real man, he was, who loved his people and would do anything for 'em, he would. No, I never heard his name like all the others, 'cause he were so good he stood out by himself, and when he was spoken of as me Lord Abbot, everybody knew whom you meant. He had a lovely house here at Brundall, with chapel and all, right by the river it stood, over there on that bank where the *Marguerite II* is berthed, and when he was sayin' his Mass, he could look now and again out o' the window and see the river and the green trees, and thank God for makin' the world so beautiful. Yes, it's gone now, 'bor. Gone these long years, and nobody's alive what can remember 'em. 'E was always called by the people here, the Bishop o' Brundall, and he carries that name to this day.

'Accordin' to the tales what's still told of him, he used to bless this river, and everybody connected with it, and twice a year he'd have his altar boat out and say his Mass whilst the rowers rowed him up and down the river, blessing the people who lined the banks as he passed along. He did use to keep his boats both at St Benet's or St Benedict's Abbey – whichever you do like, for it's all the same – and it was nothin' for him to slip across through South Walsham by his coach and ferry the Bure. Well, every twice a year, on 24 June and 18 September, he did use to come up and down the river in all his full robes and bless the people and the river. On the first trip he always blessed the babies, 'cause it was their festival at that time, Christmas day, which me old fayther did use to tell me always come on 23 June, but, Lord bless 'ee, they've so played about with the calendar, at least that's what I understand, that one doesn't know whether the day before tomorrow is goin' to be next Sunday, or yesterday is tomorrow week. And I do say as it oughtn't to be allowed, 'cause it *is* so confusin'. Don't know where ye are, so to speak.

'Well, as I was sayin', he died and did die beloved of everybody in this county, and he did love his people so that he said he would always bless them even when he was dead and gone. And he has done it. Twice a year he comes up this river, first on 24 June and the second time on 18 September. Always on his same wonderful barge covered with beautiful cloths and silk carpets, and his marvellous altar all gold and white, and lighted with candles whilst he sits on a sort of throne, and carries a large silver thing in his hands like a big glistenin' star. There are twenty-eight rowers and they go by without a splash or ripple. They comes up from Buckenham and makes for Norwich. People what is sick comes down to be blessed as he goes by, and no one up this way, not even the li'l childer is afeer'd of him.

'Old Mrs Thurby, who had been a long sufferer with the rheumatics and confined to her bed for several months, was carried down here to the riverside only last June, and when he went by he blessed her, and she is now fair wholly cured.

'A small girl about nine had a fright when a cow went mad and raced down the street here, back three year ago. Everybody was panicky and ran in different directions, there was a bad rush, she wasn't able to get out of the way in time, and the cow knocked her down, and from that moment she went stone blind, she did. It was a terrible case, and the poor little child nearly cried herself into her grave.

'The followin' year a friend said to her mother: "You let Alice come and stay with me for a bit, and maybe I'll cure her."

'Her mother, after a deal o' persuadin' give in, and the little girl went to stay with the friend. A week before the Lord Abbot was expected up-river, she told the child that one night she should stay up late and come down to the river and "see" the dear Lord go by.

'The night come round and little Alice was taken down to the riverbank, and told to pray for her sight to come back. The excitement of the child was wonderful, and some of us shook our heads about it, 'cause it would have been a terrible thing if, after all, she was to be disappointed. Some people is so stupid, and ain't got the sense of a "dickie" (donkey). Still, she were a very pious woman and did believe very truly, she did.

'We was all gathered together on the bank, and knelt down when the church clock struck twelve. It was a dark night and no moon and no stars, but we knelt there and waited. Presently we heard some bells tinklin' in the distance down stream, and after a while we see the Lord Abbot on his barge comin' round the bend. The lights on his altar lighted up the river, and slowly they came closer and closer. Just as they was passin', the child's friend said to her: "Look, Alice, there he is! Ask him now. Quick!"

'And the little girl turned in his direction and cranin' her head forward called out in her shrill, pipey little voice: "Dear Lord, give me back my sight please."

'The rowers stopped and rested on their oars, and the Lord Abbot turned to see who it was a-callin'. When he see the little girl with

her chubby little arms outstretched towards him, he stood up, and blessed her with the beautiful silver stag he was holdin' in his hands, and made the sign o' the Cross towards her.

'Suddenly the child screamed. "Mummy! Mummy! I can see! I can see!" And we all fell on our knees and her too, and she cried and cried like a baby. We all did have lumps in our throats, too, we had. Then he smiled and sat down, and the rowers continued their work.

'To say we was dumbfoundered isn't saying anything at all. We was proper staggered. Soon the percession disappeared up-stream, and we brought lanterns and had a look at the child. It was true enough. Her sight had come back, so we all went round to her mother's and knocked her up, and when she come down and see what we was all there for, she flung her arms around the little girl, and cried like some o' the rest o' them. It was a miracle right enough, and Alice is a big girl now of thirteen, and can see as well as you or me. I only mentions this case special, 'cause it is wonderful, really wonderful, to think what faith, blind faith – if you like – can do.

'But bless 'ee, 'bor, those two cases is only a smatterin' o' what he has done for his people here.'

I made, on the strength of this honest fellow's story, several enquiries amongst the local inhabitants, and found that some had never heard of it; others looked very hard and either changed the subject or shut up like Willum's clam. I was more successful a little further afield, and in Witteringham I discovered an old lady, aged but truthful, who gave me the following version, in the lead-up to which I was exceedingly discreet and careful not to let slip any suggestions or put any leading questions, and this is what Mrs Germaine told me:

'Long years ago there was once a very holy man who was Bishop of Norwich and Lord Abbot of St Benet's-at-Holm, and every year he blessed the rivers Bure and Yare in order to keep away any evil spirits who might beset the people in this part of his diocese, because, as you may or may not be aware, sir, the spirits of evil never did like water. It cleanses the spirit-body, and the physical-body as well, and that is why in the Roman church water is blessed and sprinkled on the people, even today. And this very saintly bishop always used to travel by water when he could, and kept his boats up and down both rivers. Sometimes he would be rowed all the way from Norwich down past Brundall, and on to Reedham, across Breydon Water, and up the Bure past Stokesby to Acle and St Benet's Abbey, and from there up to Horning, Wroxham and Colitshall.' (She knew her topography all right.)

'Well, when he was alive he was so holy that he performed the most wonderful miracles, and he so loved his people that he promised before he died to look after them when he was gone. And he has continued to do so for the last nine hundred years and more. Twice a year he comes right up the Yare to Norwich, and is first seen either at Brundall or Buckenham, where he used to keep his boats. As soon as he arrives at Pull's Ferry at Norwich he disappears. Pull's Ferry in days gone by used to be the water-gate to the cathedral, though many don't know it. Only a year or two back he cured a child of

76

blindness as he passed up the river, and the numbers of people suffering from rheumatism, skin disease, and all manners of chronic complaints he has cured would fill a book.

'No, I can't say I have ever seen him myself, but that's my own fault. I think I'm a little bit frightened of spiritual things and things I can't understand, but it's all true enough, as several people will tell you about it who have actually seen him, not once, but many times.'

At Buckenham, famous for its 'Cockatrice', I obtained a similar story, differing only in the telling by the personal colouring of the teller. George Peters is a very straight man, truthful, kind, sympathetic and well-beloved by his friends in those parts. He actually showed me the very spot where tradition holds that the Bishop's boats were kept, and he says that it is generally believed that when the Lord Abbot died he took his special boat with him, and comes back in it every time he visits his diocese.

Fired with enthusiasm, two others, the Very Reverend Dr James Gesgoine, D.D., and Stephen Andrews, D.Sc., M.A., and I decided to try it out and see if it were possible to verify these psychic happenings to our own satisfaction. Accordingly, on 24 June last year we arrived at Brundall, had a light meal at the Yare Hotel, and put over to the other side with the idea of doing some fishing, because there is just at this bend of the river some very excellent sport.

It was a perfect night, the sky bright with stars, and the river reflecting their silver scintillations in its mirror surface. All around was still and quiet except for an occasional screech-owl, and the nightingales, which were just beginning to tune up. The trees were still, and only now and again a gentle zephyr softly soughing through the branches stirred the mountain ash to leafy music.

Just about 11.30 p.m. a great stillness fell upon the place, and although it was still and quiet before, yet this was much more intense. Like the 'biblical' darkness that could be felt, so it was with this extraordinary quiet. The owls had ceased, and the nightingales too. A curious feeling came over each one of us, as though we were approaching some august presence and it might arrive any moment. To those who know what is meant by the term 'psychic', that is exactly what the atmosphere was. It had changed almost without perception from the gentle, free, still and placid quietude to that tense almost electric pressure with a feeling of 'dense' tranquillity, so often associated with and preceding a supernormal manifestation.

Wider and wider awake we became, for we were on the alert for anything that might happen. We could descry some dark outlines of people moving on the opposite bank, villagers who had come down to be cured, or to give praise from their grateful and loving hearts for the many favours already received.

At last Dr Andrews exclaimed in a loud whisper: 'Hullo! Hear that?'

We strained every nerve to try and catch some sound, but could hear nothing. We listened intently, and, lowering the end of my stethoscope into the water, I heard what the unaided ear could never have – distant music, but very clear and sweet. It came and it went, rising and falling in gentlest cadences, and then we saw a faint glow coming slowly up the river towards us. Presently we could see the faint light stretching away back for some distance, and gradually it all came nearer. The moments were like centuries, and a feeling of pent-up excitement was beginning to make itself felt, by a tingling of one's nerve-plates all over the limbs and body; especially was it noticeable in the hair, which felt as though it were being smoothed with an electric brush. As the light approached so the details within it began to fill in, and in a few moments we could see as though through a thin curtain the spirit outlines of a very long boat rowed by a crew of spirit-men all clothed in white. The bow of the boat was moving through the water quite fast, and yet there was no wave, not even the faintest undulation.

In the prow of the vessel was a man robed in the orthodox cope and mitre of a bishop, and seated beneath a baldicchino of superb beauty held up by four fine golden uprights. Six torchbearers stood around wearing red cassocks and lace rochets, whilst two thurifers stood swinging their censers on each side of the prow. Behind the torchbearers was a small but very elaborate altar with an array of nearly three hundred lighted wax tapers, and a crucifix standing on a tabernacle in the centre. The altar itself appeared to be of white marble, and its hangings were of fine linen edged with gold.

The most striking object of all was the Lord Abbot himself, who had the most marvellous face I have ever seen in my life. It was the face of what one would conceive to be that of a perfect angel with the most wonderfully chiselled features imaginable. His eyes were full of tenderness and affection, whilst his expression was firm and yet seraphic. In his hands he held a large silver monstrance, which glistened like some celestial light sending out an aurora as though it were illuminated from within. In the centre of this superb holy vessel was the Host, and as the Bishop passed and saw the people gathered on the opposite bank he turned, and smiling as no human face has ever done, raised the monstrance with both hands and blessed them with it by making the sign of the Cross with it in their direction.

To say that we were thrilled is to leave it almost unsaid. We were transported with a joy far transcending anything I personally have ever before experienced. Slowly this altared barge, followed by a fleet of six others, passed up the river, their dim, self-contained light glinting on the water as they made the bend beyond the village, and then gradually faded out on their journey to Norwich. Nothing more beautiful can the human mind conceive than this glorious vision of a spiritual phenomenon. Some people imagine that all such things must of necessity be diabolical, but that is sheer ignorance begotten of inexperience. If anyone has any doubt about it, let them go to Brundall as we did, and enlighten their mental darkness, and they will come away rejoicing.

It must be remembered that all people are not sufficiently psychically tuned to perceive these manifestations, but it is well worth trying, and they must on no account let themselves feel disappointment if their efforts are not attended with success at the first attempt. They must try again.

Acle

'Never heard of the ghost of Acle Bridge?' The man put down his tankard in surprise, and wiped his mouth on a large red handkerchief. The tone of his voice made me feel as though I ought to be well ashamed of my colossal ignorance, and I am certain he quite expected me to crumple up and sneak away with my tail well between my legs.

'Never,' I replied, scenting a story over the horizon, 'I should like to hear about it.'

The man looked into his empty tankard, so I had it replenished immediately.

'They won't talk about it round here,' he went on, 'and some'll swear they've never seen it and have, whilst others'll swear it's all lies because they haven't. But it's true enough, you can take it from me, and if you don't believe it – and, mind, I'm not asking you to – come along here on 7 April any year you like, and see it for yourself. Don't go hanging around suspicious-like, but just be about here and arrange your walk to bring you near the bridge, about 12.30 ack-emma. Another point I must tell you is that for some reason or other it's always more evident when it's raining. Don't ask me why, but it is so.

'Of course, a lot o' people aren't aware that they used to hang highwaymen on that bridge and let 'em dangle over the river, but they did. The practice was discontinued about Queen Anne's time, but many's the cut-throat, sneak-thief, footpad and murderer who has stepped off that parapet to an unknown address. You may have noticed the red splash on the outside of the stone-work on the up-river side. That's blood, and they can't get it out. They've tried everything. They've even chipped the face of the stone away, but it's been there the day after, just as bad. When a murderer – and only a murderer – took the drop, he would sometimes bleed violently from the nose or the ears, sometimes both, and if that blood touched the bridge, it was a sure sign that the real assassin was laughing up his sleeve somewhere else, but of course it was too late to call the innocent man back. A small matter, but there you are. This is very good beer they sell here, 'bor.' (I had noticed it.) 'Well, as I was saying, it was a great event when a feller paid the price, and people'd come from far and near to see old "Jack Ketch" come and do his stuff.

'In those days they never used to execute people in the town, but took 'em a little way out, like as they did in Lunnon. There they used to lug 'em on a cart or a hurdle and take 'em over to Tyburn Tree, what was a triangular gibbet, so's they could hang three at a time if needs be, and stood just a few feet beyond where the Marbil Arch is now. I've got a picture of it somewhere in a book at home, and I could show it to you, if you wished. Here they used to bring the condemned man down to the bridge because the bridge wasn't considered to be in the town, and he'd have to mount the parapet, the rope was slipped over his head, the knot under his left ear for certainty, his hands and feet tied, and a long line attached to his ankles. When all was ready, they carried this line around the river bank, and, at a given signal, the hangman pulled his feet off the parapet, and the victim twisted and struggled in mid-air, and the more he struggled the more he hung himself, and the deader he got. Of course he never felt nothing, it was too quick, what was more than his own victim could brag about. I should imagine the Billington of those days must have had plenty of work and made a bit, seeing that they used to hang for stealing a sheep or even a groat, what was fourpence (in case you don't know). They used to hang also for fortune-telling, necromancers they called 'em.

'Do you know the last time anyone was hung for witchcraft in this country? You don't? Well – it was about 1749, and it was either at Acle or Nottingham, I can't quite remember which, but they strung up a Mrs Morris, who was a widder, and her little nine-year-old daughter at the same time. Let me see – no? Nottingham? Nottingham? Yes, it was Nottingham, not Acle.

'But Nottingham isn't Acle Bridge, is it, and I was going to tell you about the ghost there.

'Well, when good King James was King – you know the one I mean, the son of William the Conqueror and father of Pope Joan – well, there was a very wicked man who lived near here in a big house what used to stand over there where them trees are – gone now, years and years ago, and that was haunted, too – and he was the wickedest old devil that ever traded in these 'ere parts. He was a corn chandler by profession, and loaded his scales, cooked his measures, and robbed everybody as openly as he could. A shocking old brute. Beat his wife, they said, to death, but I daresay as she asked for it. Most women who come by their end in that way generally do. He starved his children and was a disgrace to his sex. Never washed, ate his food with his hands, never used no knife and fork, and wore his filthy old clothes until they hung in rags about him. A perfect little gentleman and no mistake. His name was Josiah Burge, and oh, how everybody hated him.

'He was tried for the murder of his first wife, but got off because he squared the doctor to swear as she died from heart disease or the dyspepsia or something, and not from the hiding he gave her with a bit o' lead pipe in the back parlour of his corn shop. Her screams brought half the town round the house, and then he rushed out and yelled at them to fetch the doctor, and quick. Thinking as she was only ill, they slowly dispersed, and someone went for the doctor. No one ever knew what really was the matter with her, but she lingered for a week and then hopped it. Some kind friend started gossiping, and old man Burge was arrested for murder. He stood his trial at Norwich and was acquitted on the doctor's evidence that she died of heart disease. But it didn't end there.

'She had a brother what knew of how her husband had treated her, and when he heard that Burge wasn't going to swing for it after all, he vowed he would swing for his brother-in-law instead.

'One dark night, a 7 April, he lay in wait for his man, as he was coming home in his pony trap from Yarmouth, and when it was in the middle of the bridge, he sprung out ant, seizing the horse's head, stopped him, and then, springing up on the step, he got hold of Burge, who tried to beat him off with the handle of his whip. Luggin' him out of the trap, he forced him back across the parapet of the bridge, and cut his throat from ear to ear, and stabbed him all over with a huge pointed butcher's knife, the blood running down all over the stonework. Then he jumped into the pony-cart and drove off as hard as he could go, and left Yarmouth that morning early on a ship he'd signed on for the previous day.

'When he came back years later from the East, he learned of his brother-in-law's death, which of course he pretended he knew nothing about, and that a local man of not too good a character, and who was known to have been a bitter enemy of old Burge's, had swung for the murder. In the following year his curiosity got too strong for him, and he longed to go down to the bridge and see the spot where he had done old man Burge in. It was an impulse he could not resist, although he tried to fight within himself against going near it, but he wasn't strong enough, and against his will he went.

'It was a clear night and as he stood there leaning against the very spot where he had revenged his sister, thinking it all over again in his mind and glad that he'd done it, suddenly a skeleton sprung on him out of nowhere and – forcing him back against the coaming – where his assailant got the strength from goodness alone knows, seeing as he had no muscles at all and was only bones – he left his body hanging half over the bridge, with its throat cut from ear to ear and stabbed all over, and his blood gushed down all over the stones.

'Every night of 7 April this awful crime is committed, the same as it was on the first occasion, and the following morning the wall of the bridge is stained with blood.

'They do say, them as have seen it, that the skeleton is the man what swung for the murder and never did it, and that his victim is Mrs Burge's brother.'

I was so interested that I made enquiries, and after a lot of trouble and patient searching, discovered in the *Chronicles of the Norwich Assizes*, that one Josiah Burge was tried for the murder of his wife at Acle, and was discharged on medical evidence that she died from heart disease.

In the *Archives of H.M. Crowners for the Counties of Norfolk and Suffolk* it states that 'an inquest was held upon the dead body of one Josiah Burge, who was found wilfully, brutally and foully murdered, by being stabbed to death on Acle Bridge on the night of April, 7th by some person or persons unknown.'

That it was a terrible retribution goes without saying, but that it is true is much more important.

This awful outrage has been witnessed by many. One, the Right Honourable Earl of Vauxhall, states in a letter written to his brother, in 1827, as follows:

'We were late getting back and . . . were about to cross over the river Bure at Acle, when suddenly the leaders and wheelers came to a dead halt. Nothing would budge them, and they trembled and whinnied alarmingly. It was very awkward, dear brother, because we had to get the ladies home. Lady Jessica began to cry, and Monica, dear soul, soon joined her, fearful that their delay might give rise to anxiety at the Manor. A man was standing at the corner of the bridge carelessly leaning against the wall, when suddenly before our very eyes a huge live skeleton, glowing with an uncanny light, sprung on him, forcing his head back over the parapet, and stabbed him all over. Lord Monty, our coachman Berris, and I, rushed forward to try and seize the murderer, but on arriving at the spot, not a soul was to be seen, but there was fresh blood all over the stone.

'That it was an apparition and a terrible one to witness there is no question. As soon as we had returned to the drag, the ladies, who fortunately were inside and therefore had not witnessed this gruesome and hair-raising spectacle, brightened up, and were rejoiced when the horses were quieted and the coach moved on over the bridge.'

Parson Battle, writing in the *Norwich and County Gazette* of May 1879, says:

'Acle Bridge was once the scene of two terrible murders, each one a crime of revenge. Several of my acquaintances aver that they have actually seen one of the murders re-enacted several times, and that it happens every year on the night of 7th April.'

I went back to Acle to try and find the man who first informed me about it, and after several unsuccessful attempts ran across him in the tiny hamlet of Nowhere. (Don't laugh. Look on your map.) He was watching a game of bowls when I found him, and we wandered back into Acle and went down on to the bridge for a yarn. He soon opened up on the topic of the apparition, and whilst we were leaning against the parapet, we noticed a man go by who appeared to recognise us. He was a curiously dressed person, and his face was very drawn and sunken, his eyes especially. As he sauntered slowly by I caught his glance, and our eyes met. That he knew me, or thought he did, there was no question, so I turned to my informative friend and said in an undertone:

'Who's that? Do you know him?'

'Who?' he enquired.

'Why that chap just gone by. I won't turn round, he may still be looking.'

'Who are you referring to?' he asked, looking stupidly at me.

'Why, the fellow who went past a moment ago.'

'Do you mean that fellow down on the bank fishing?' he replied, indicating an ardent Walton below the bridge.

'No, the man with the cadaverous-looking face that has just walked by.'

'Come. Come, old friend. You're dreaming. There's not a soul anywhere about here except that Johnnie with his rod.'

'Do you mean to tell me you didn't see that weird-looking card go by a moment since?'

'No one has passed us on this bridge since we've been standing here,' he answered. 'Look around and see for yourself.' I did so, and – there was the man I had seen at the end of the bridge, looking over.

'There he is,' I replied quickly. 'Tell me now he isn't there.'

'Well, I'm hanged, 'bor. There's not a soul about, nowhere. You're certainly dreaming.'

'Do you mean to——' but I dried up, for at that moment the man in question had started to walk back. 'Look,' I continued, 'he's coming this way.'

We lingered there as the man passed us again, and this time he looked straight at me again. I followed him with my eyes.

'Look now. He's stopped and is looking over into the water again. I'm going to speak to him.'

'Don't be a fule!' exclaimed my friend, impatiently. 'You've got him on your mind. Come back!'

'I'm going,' I answered, nothing loth. 'I'm going to speak to him. He interests me. You come along, too.'

He came, but very reluctantly, and tried his best to dissuade me, evidently convinced that I was seeing things.

When the man saw us approaching he looked away, but remained where he was. I shall never forget his face. It was so sallow and painfully thin, like an advanced case of malignant disease with imminent dissolution written right across it. My friend saw my determination and came along, but tried hard to convince me that it was not always a wise policy to speak to people one did not know. But somehow I felt this stranger was interested in me and wanted to speak. My friend could not make me out at all. As we came up to him he was leaning with his back to the wall. His eyes met mine again, and as instantly he faded clean into nothingness and was gone.

'Didn't I tell you there was nobody there?' And just at that moment he was right. The man had vanished like a puff from my pipe. I still wonder who he was or might have been.

Burgh St Peter

You would scarce believe as you turn to the left into the Waveney out of Oulton Dyke that that beautiful little spot on your right could be haunted, and yet every 2 May as the clock strikes the midnight hour a most engaging and holding apparition manifests itself outside the ivy-clad church, which nestles in the trees on the little rill above the river bank.

Burgh St Peter is very, very ancient. The parish register dates back to AD 1557, and the church perhaps four or five hundred years prior to that.

The church, which curiously enough is dedicated to St Mary, is one of the most unique in the country, in that it is one hundred and ten feet long and only fourteen wide. The nave inside looks like an aisle, or a corridor, it is so narrow, and the roof is thatched. The tower is one of the most unique in the kingdom, successive generations having added a bit at a time until five storeys were raised one above the other, each one being smaller than the one below. The top one supported a short spire, but it was later removed, and its capstone and finial remain in the graveyard.

Now, the man who built the original church, AD 1101 (c.), was hard up, and one day exclaimed impatiently: 'Ah me!' (or words to that effect) 'would that I were rich. I'd give anything if I could only be rich.'

The words were no sooner uttered than an elderly gentleman whom he had not seen standing behind him, touched him on the shoulder, and a cold shiver ran down his spine. Turning around, he discovered he was not alone, but the old man said:

'Don't be alarmed, friend. What are you in need of?'

Now Adam Morland was a little ashamed at being overheard by a stranger, and blurted out the first thing that came into his mind.

'Nothing,' he answered, not liking the appearance very much of this apparently harmless and good-natured old gentleman.

'Oh, but I thought I heard you wish for riches just now.'

'Well – what if I did? Can't a man mutter to himself without being eavesdropped, Mr Inquisitive?'

Most people would have felt so insulted by such treatment that they would have departed in high dudgeon, but not so in this case. This benevolent old gentleman was not one to be put off by another's passing spleen, and only smiled kindly, and toying with his stick on the ground, said in a very kindly voice:

'Let me help you, friend. It matters not in what way, I can help you, I'm sure, and I will.'

'It's very kind of you, dear sir,' replied Adam Morland, beginning to feel the truth of the old saw that the kind word turneth away wrath, 'but I could not accept money from a stranger.'

'No, quite,' said the philanthropic friend,' I quite understand, but let me lend it to you. No interest. All that I ask is that you will one day repay me.'

'Repay you? Of course, I'd promise that. But I cannot understand you not requiring any interest for your money.'

'Ah, my dear friend, I am not in need of interest. I have so much money that I am only too glad to have the opportunity of helping my fellow creatures, to whom I am very devoted.'

'I think you're a splendid soul!' exclaimed friend Adam, 'I am very sorry I spoke so curtly to you just now.'

'I pray you not to mention it,' replied the old man. 'How much do you want?'

'About twelve thousand pounds,' answered Adam.

'Twelve thousand? Twelve thousand? Oh, that is simple. I thought you were going to say five hundred thousand. A very different matter, but – I could have managed it. Can you write?' he said, pulling out a scroll.

'No, I fear me I cannot.'

'Never mind,' exclaimed the dear old gentleman. 'Impress your thumb on this wax. That's sufficient.'

And Mr Adam Morland pressed his thumb well down on it, and thought it burnt him, it felt so hot.

'Ta-ta!' said the old fellow, and ambled off.

When our friend arrived home, a large packing-case was standing outside his front door, so he dragged it into his house, where, curious to find out what it could possibly be, he made a big hole near the top with a hatchet, and a stream of golden money poured out on to the floor.

'That's quick work,' thought Adam, and stooping to pick up some of the money, found it was still very hot, as though it had just been minted. He carefully examined some of the pieces, and came to the conclusion that they must have just come from the moulds, since they were so hot and new. His next move was to dig a large hole under his floor and hide the money, because it would not have been politic for the world outside to learn of all this sudden wealth. It would not only be difficult to explain, but doubly so to guard against thievery.

Now, our friend had been abroad and travelled in many lands, and on one occasion when he was shipwrecked he fell on his knees on the deck of the sinking ship and prayed that if he were saved he would build a church to the glory of God before he died. He now set about his promise as quickly as possible, and in a short while the church was built. It was not exactly a cathedral, but large enough to serve the countryside around the hamlet of Burgh St Peter, and it was dedicated to St Mary. On the foundations of this church stands the present one which has already been described.

As soon as Morland's church was finished, the Lord Abbot of St Benet's-at-Holm consecrated it, but its founder 'tooke sicke of a fever and dyede, and was interred within the sacred walls.'

For some time prior to his decease, an elderly gentleman whom nobody knew had been seen in the neighbourhood, and hanging around Adam Morland's door. He held in his hand a scroll of parchment, but would not speak to anybody. He appeared to be very distressed, and on the day of the funeral he became very excited and followed the cortège to the church, but would not enter the sacred portal, preferring apparently to stand outside with this scroll in his hand and walk agitatedly up and down. As the body was lowered into the grave he was heard to swear an awful oath that he would wait for Adam Morland until the day of his resurrection. And as he cursed, Morland's house went up in flames and roared like a blast furnace.

The old man was seen sitting on a stone outside the church door when the service was over, and when the church was locked up that night he was still sitting there. The sexton went up to him to see if he could be helpful in any way, and when the old man looked up, the poor villager had the shock of his life. The old man's head was a skull with a glowing fire inside it, and then he saw that the rest was a skeleton, and he fled panic-stricken to the village and called up the priest and the people. They thought he had gone mad, but followed him back to the church, the priest, armed with holy water and crucifix, leading the way.

As soon as they arrived, the old man saw what was about to happen and grew frightened. The priest advanced with the asperger and crucifix held out in front of him, and suddenly they saw the skeleton stand up and vanish in a flash of red flame, leaving behind a dense cloud of brimstone vapour, almost suffocating everyone present.

For years afterwards that skeleton waited outside that porch with the scroll clenched in his bony hand, waiting, waiting, patiently waiting for the body of Adam Morland.

Then came the day when the old church gave place to the present one, and it was thought that the devil would cease his vigil, but not a bit of it. He even went further and brought a company of similar chthonic brethren, arranging them in a circle around the outside wall of the churchyard, to help him catch Mr Morland, deceased, if he tried any tricks of attempting to get away with the congregation without being spotted.

And there he still comes on every anniversary of the death of the man to whom he gave the money, and who gave him his soul with the seal of his thumb on the wax. Had he known what the man he trusted was going to do with the money, of course the church would never have materialised, but when it was finished its consecration protected it for ever from his lethal hands. He could not even destroy it as he did Morland's house, so all that was left to him was to wait and bide his time, which he still does, and it is very extraordinary how well-endowed he is with apparently everlasting patience.

Several attempts have been made in byegone days to lay this visitor from Hadesian climes, but four Lord Abbots, seven archdeacons, five bishops, and heaven alone knows how many dignitaries of the church and state have endeavoured to send this unhealthy person about his business, but in vain.

In the *Epistolas Ecclesiasticum et Apostolicum*, of March 1501 AD, para. 43, page 9, we read the following, which is translated from the Latin:

'I, by the Grace of God, Guilliame, Lord Abbot of Norwiche and St Benet's-at-Holm, do hereby authorise that the second day of May in each year shall be in this my province a holy day to be set aside for fasting and prayer, to pray for the repose of the soul of one Adam Morland, founder of the church of St Mary, at Burgh St Peter, and that on this same day shall be made a pilgrimage by all those who are able, and not held by sickness, to attend at the said church for the purpose of driving away the evil spirit which haunteth the ground adjacent to the said church of St Mary. Branches of fir together with palms specially blessed on the preceding Palm Sunday shall be burned at the church porch, and the sacred ashes cast upon the ground about. Then shall be intoned the "Nunc Dimittis" followed by the "De Profundis", after which a procession shall form and process around the outside of the church. The service shall terminate with the "Te Deum", the rest of the day being given over to rejoicing.'

This was evidently too much for the Old Gent., and he used to keep away for considerable periods, but in the *Gentleman's Chronicle* for September 1683, we learn 'that this skeletone doth still haunte ye olde churchyarde much, causinge grievous frightenings to timid persons and smalle children. Only last Maye it was agayne seene, by one Mary Dowdell, a woman advanced in her yeares, causinge her to lose her reasone and falle into the faintes. She lingered manie yeares and dyed insane which is greatlie to be pittyed. She left a good husbande and eleven offspringes:

> Oh, howe sadde it is to see
> A piouse woman lose her minde
> All through a seeinge such as sight
> Whiche neither was so goode nor kinde.
> Take heed ye maydens in thy youthe
> To persevere in prayer and truthe,
> Lest ere it be too late to finde
> The devil he hath turned thy minde.

And so the old legend comes about and is passed down through the ages, believed by some, scouted by others; but before passing any judgment, let us hear what John Arbuthnot Carruthers, a hard-headed business man, said of it in the *Litteras Archæologia* for July 1929:

'We came alongside at the Ferry, and decided to spend the night here. It was the evening of 2 May, and after gossiping with some villagers decided to visit the old ivy-clad church of St Mary. Sir Alexander Taunton, the famous bridge engineer; Spencer Meredith, the writer; George Inskip Wetherby, the K.C.; Lady Diana Oakland, the well-known airwoman; Neville Anderson Critt, the celebrated surgeon; Lord Edgar Staines, F.R.S.; Douglas Peterson, Esq., J.P., Sheriff for the County of Suffex, were members of my wherry party, and we decided to visit the famous church. On entering the gate we saw an old man hurrying on in front of us, but on reaching the church porch he disappeared. We were struck by his curious walk, and after visiting the interior of the building, who should we see on emerging into the light once more but the same old man. Lord Staines called out to him "Hi!" and he stopped, and in that moment of his turning around, we all saw he was a skeleton with a roll of dirty looking paper in his hand. He glared at us, and decamped away across the graves, and on giving pursuit, we could find no trace of him anywhere. He had vanished into thin air, but Lady Diana had the misfortune to slip on something and break her left ankle. This sepulchral person left behind a foul, loathsome stench, and we were glad to get back to the *Venturous*, where each of us wrote a precis of what we had seen in our diaries. The eight descriptions tally exactly, and leave no cause for doubt about this evil monster, who can reveal himself to anyone who is not of the village, for they are blessed with episcopal benedictions in perpetuity against all harm from this malevolent being. Neither will anyone see it who carries anything on him of the nature of a sacramental, such as an Agnus Dei, or a crucifix.'

There is not the slightest question that when Mr Adam Morland sold his soul to Satan, he did it without realising what he was doing, and 'Old Nick' can afford to wait.

Whenever I pass that spot as I go up the Waveney, even on a perfectly still day, with not a breath of air stirring, a cold wind blows across my face and down my back, my body gives a tremble, and I break out in a slight, chilly sweat.

I am told on the very best authority that Adam Morland passed to glory fortified with all the rights of Holy Church, so if by any chance you happen to run up against his Satanic Majesty gnashing his bony gums at the church door, keep the information to yourself, for silence is golden, and a still tongue makes a wise head.

Somerleyton

'We'll put in here for the night,' said Hubert, getting out the quant-hook and a short hitcher, and turning to a fellow on the bank who seemed to have nothing to do and plenty of time to do it in, called out:

'Hi, George!' (everybody's George to Hubert). 'Here, catch this and dig it in.'

The *Hermione* came alongside the bank and Hubert jumped ashore.

'You a'nt stoppin'?' exclaimed the yokel, with an anxious look on his face.

'Of course we are!' replied Hubert, a little surprised.

'But not tonight?'

'Why not?'

'Why not, indeed? Don't you know?'

Hubert registered increased surprise and said: 'Well, what's the matter with tonight, anyway?'

'Gradabor! He's about tonight.'

'Gradabor? Gradabor? Who the heck is Gradabor?'

The rustic dropped his voice to a gutteral whisper:

'Gradabor's the giant. He comes here every year, and he's expected tonight.'

'Well, what if he is?' enquired Hubert, 'we're not afraid of giants.' Then, turning to me, 'Are we?'

'Not on your life,' I replied, pricking up both ears and scenting romance.

'Can't you see,' went on the man, 'there's no boats here tonight. All gone away till to-morrer.'

'Here,' I said, interrupting, 'I've been told on the best authority that the beer up at the inn is exceptionally good. Let's all go up there, George, and you shall tell us all about it.'

You will scarce believe it when I tell you that that man actually hesitated, but we prevailed upon him, and leaving the yacht in the tender care of the bank, we, that is Hubert, Molyneux, the man and myself, proceeded to the pub, sat down in the old-fashioned bar, and primed George with a quart of the brownest.

'Come along now, George,' I said, 'tell us all about it. Never mind the others. I'm very deeply interested.' And this was the story:

'Gentlemen, tonight is 17 July, and everyone shuts himself up in his house, and early too. Fancy you never havin' heard o' Gradabor. Gradabor was Blunderbore's twin. Blunderbore, you've heard of him? Well, he lived in the west, down Cornwall way, and Gradabor still lives in the east of England, and this is his home. All around here is his hunting-ground. He really lives by Fritton Decoy, and once a year he wakes up and stalks all over these parts. From Belton to St Olave's, and down here to Blundestone Marshes.

'What sort of a giant is he, did you ask? Well, you can believe me or not, but when he walks about, those tall trees up on the hills are to him as blades o' grass to you. If you was to stand on the palm of his hand, you'd think you was standin' in the middle of an empty ballroom. All the year round he sleeps under ground, and comes up once in a twelvemonth, like he will tonight for a spell and blow o' fresh air. Every year it's the same. And the damage he does. It's no joke, I can tell you.

'Back about a hundred years ago, a man thought he would destroy this giant, and prepared a big pit and filled it with spikes, like Jack the Giant-Killer did when he killed Blunderbore. But Gradabor was ten times the size of Blundabore, although they were twins, and one day he happened to come along whilst this huge pit was being dug, and when the man stopped to rest on his spade for a moment, he was struck temporarily dumb with fear, for Gradabor was sittin' on the hill over there watchin' him. The giant was interested to see such a gargantuan work going on and wondered what on earth it could be for, and in his softest, gentlest tone, which shook the neighbourhood, enquired:

'"Hullo! What are you diggin' such a great pit for?"

'"Nothin'," said the man, behaving most uncomfortable.

'"Oh-ho-ho!" said the giant, his suspicions being roused at once, and thinkin' of what happened to his brother in Cornwall. "This looks as though it is being prepared for me."

'He leaned forward and picked up the man between his finger and thumb, and stretching his arm at full length, held the man up several thousand feet and squeezed him to death. He squeezed him so hard that not a particle of moisture was left in the body, and when he rubbed him between his fingers, the man's whole body was resolved to a powder, like as when you rub out a moth. His blood fell to the ground like red rain, and the spot where it fell is known as Bloodman's Corner, which lies just over there behind the park and beyond Lound. Every year on 19 November it rains a shower of blood there,

94

The tomb of the Norfolk giant Robert Hales in Somerton Churchyard –
see footnote on page 99.

in the daytime too, and a great shadow extends across the sky from
the direction of Somerleyton. That's Gradabor's arm. When I was a
nipper and was inclined to be wilful, I used to be told they would
give me to the giant. That did it!

'He sleeps over yonder beyond Fritton Decoy, and those large
mounds at Mill-Hill and Bell-Hill what you calls tumulusses are due
to him underneath. He wakes up once a year and tramps around
looking for food and drink. Sometimes he has the nightmares and
snorts and grunts, and the wind howls and the rain comes down like
walkin' sticks. There used to be a village over near Bell-Hill called
Belton Minor, and one night he got up, shook himself, didn't look
where he was steppin' and the next mornin' it was gone, church and
all. Pushed it right into the earth, he did, and not a soul was left to tell
the tale.

'Many years ago, he woke up starving, and reaching out he picked
up Farmer Gauder's herd of Frisian cattle and ate 'em all one at a
time and alive. Of course, one can't do anythin'. One wishes one
could, but there you are, as the sayin' goes. If I was you I wouldn't
stay here tonight. Go away and come back tomorrow night if you
like, but don't stay in these parts tonight. I'm only warnin' you. Yes,
this is good ale, an' I don't really mind if I do. Thank you very much,
'bor. What else did you ask – do I know anything about him? Oh,

lots.' And turning to another agricultural labourer who was talking to some friends, said: 'Here, Shandy, I want yer!' The man in question came over, and our informant and well-wisher added, 'Tell 'em, Shandy. Tell these gentlemen 'bout the giant. I don't think they quite believe me.'

Shandy cleared his throat, looked at his friend, and then at us, and asked:

'Just arrived? Well, I wouldn't stay tonight if I was you. You never know. Is your boat tied up alongside? It is: then I'd get in it and move it away. He'll be down this way in a couple of hours 'bor. It isn't worth it. Two year ago he trod down all the reeds between Blunderstone and St Olaves. Always walks by the river, he does, and I wouldn't be in a boat down this way when he goes by for a king's ransom, I wouldn't. Who is he? No one knows, but I have heard tell he's in league with the "Old Gentleman' himself, because a curious thing happens when he's comin'. The church bells ring. Peal after peal.

'No one in the village rings 'em. They rings of their own accord without no one touchin' them. When we hears them bells we knows it's a warnin', and he's on his way. One year he found a wherry unloadin' ballast at the ferry, and he just picked it up and put it over on Breydon, and when the fellers on board woke up in the mornin', they found themselves where he had put them overnight. I don't think he means no harm. It's just he's so big he can't see where he's goin' and the damage he's causin'. Don't you stay tonight, 'bor! If I was you I'd put off and go down the Waveney a bit. Pull in somewhere down there, 'cause he never crosses the water. He's never been known to go over to th' other side o' river, and you'd be perfectly safe there.'

Turning around, he called over Stingy, another friend of his.

'Stingy, what about old Gradabor tonight? These gents here want to spend the night alongside. What say you?'

Stingy, a nice red-haired, pleasant-faced person, looked at us dubiously, scratched his scrubby chin, and said:

'You get away in good time 'bor. Take my advice. Get over th' other side o' water whilst you can. After tonight it'll be all right. I've never seen him myself, but I've heard enough from them as have, and I wouldn't stay this side o' the river tonight for nothin'. I always goes across, myself. Wouldn't catch me in Somerleyton tonight. I knows better than that.'

'Where do you go?' we asked, getting inquisitive.

'Oh, there's generally some as goes across out o' the way and I goes with 'em.'

96

'Now look here,' I said, 'you come aboard with us and we'll push across to the other side, and sit up and watch for him. How's that?'

'Sounds all right, 'bor. You come too, Maggot,' addressing the first man.

'Well, I don't mind, if Shandy'll come too,' he replied.

Shandy took a deal of coaxing, but eventually it was agreed that, for a 'dollar a-piece' the three men would come with us to the opposite side of the river and spend the night. We took a gallon jar of ale with us, and we all went aboard. There was Shandy, Stingy and Maggot, Hubert, Molyneux and myself, so we made a merry party and repaired to the yacht, where we threw a spread of bully-omelette, cheese and beer, and some canned fruit to follow, tailing off with coffee and apples. The meal was a great success, and to see those hefty men eat was a sight to be remembered. You'd have thought they hadn't had a square meal for years.

After supper, we untied our bow-line, and pushed across to the opposite bank, right into the reeds, whilst one of the men hopped ashore and pushed our quant-hook into the turf.

It was certainly a weird night. One of those nights when anything could happen, and our three guests were decidedly uneasy. Their extraordinary behaviour when we first met them I felt was perhaps due to a little local vanity, giving them the opportunity of setting their stage, and performing not only for our edification, but their own, but it wasn't so after all. They were genuinely squeamish about the whole thing and I changed my opinion, but I could not make out their conception of this super-giant, which evidently had some basis of truth, if it wasn't easy to fathom or trace its origin. Here were three hefty men, with certainly no axes to grind, all genuinely terrified of this Brobdingnagian monster whom they credited with the most horrifying misdeeds, and evidently a very useful person on to whom they could lay the blame for anything and everything that went wrong, or in any way went amiss with them.

One very certain fact was that whatever, whoever, or whenever this colossus of inquiry was, his presence in these parts did not seem bad enough to cause them to evacuate his territory. You or I would have very quickly removed our lares and penates to a more accept-able and peaceful part, and seeing that on the other side of the river one could be quite safe, it is curious that they still preferred to remain in the danger zone, when by a very little effort they could have preserved themselves from the annual risk of complete extermination.

The night was clear, the stars twinkled and shone brightly in promise of a fine morrow, and not a fleck was in the sky. George threw

97

over a line with a float on it to beguile the hours of waiting, and we all sat around in the saloon and smoked. What a perfect evening it was! The river glided by in silent sympathy, and a gentle zephyr, soughing quietly through the reeds, lightly fanned our faces when we came outside.

We had come up now and were lolling on the deck, and presently a breeze sprang up. It blew from the east and moaned as it greeted the trees around us.

Suddenly it grew and grew until it blew with almost hurricane force. The sky had clouded partly over and the moaning of the wind in the trees like a lost soul trying to find its way home, gave place to a slight misgiving that our calculations for the weather forecast were going to let us down. There was a long, deep rumble in the distant sky, and intermittent flashes illuminated the eastern heavens. The rumblings increased in intensity, and the sinister nimbus that came up from the horizon had by now stolen stealthily overhead, and extended far away into the sou'-west. The stars were gone, and the night became stuffy and the air like sponge.

Whoomph! Whoom-m-ph! Several blinding flashes lighted up everything around us and the crashes nearly split our ears. The sky began to weep, and presently huge drops were falling, and in less than a minute it was raining long hitchers, fire-irons and fishing-rods. It came down as I have never seen it before in England. It was real tropical rain, and the terrific wind spread it out like a water curtain in a theatre. It was almost impossible to remain on deck, so we had foregathered once more in the saloon.

Then someone asked:

'Where's Maggot?'

'Where's Stingy?'

'Where's Shandy?'

But there was no need to ask. At the first clap of thunder they had bolted as one man off the yacht and away across the meads. Where they went it is impossible to say, but I'll stake my solemn Davey it wasn't to their homes across the water.

Gradabor certainly 'did his stuff' properly, and with a vengeance, for he had walked very thoughtfully through the park, levelling some very fine old trees in his stride. Some people are so careless.

The following day broke finer than ever, with a Neapolitan sky overhead, and everything looking very much the fresher for the good wash-down it had had overnight, so we crossed the river once more, tied up alongside the Ferry, and went 'oop t' tha' poob. There were our friends of the night before, and full of it.

'Well!' I said, addressing Maggot. 'You're a fine crowd and no mistake! Leaving us there in the lurch like that and running for your lives.'

'Oh, 'bor,' exclaimed Stingy, trying to placate us with his stupid belief. 'We thought he was comin' across, and we nipped it.'

'But what about us?' I replied, feeling very annoyed at the fellow's cheek.

''Bor,' he replied, 'you'd never understand. He come right down across the park. Did a lot o' damage, he did. Then he stumped right down through the marshes all along by the river, and then went home.'

And, will you believe me, he looked me straight in the eyes as he said it, and appeared to lend his own conviction to everything he said.

Anyway, if ever you're down Somerleyton way on or about 17 July, keep a good look-out for Gradabor, and don't forget, well to the other side of the river.

Editor's Note

It may be entirely irrelevant to Charles Sampson's story of the Giant of Somerleyton that Robert Hales, the famous Norfolk Giant, lies in the churchyard at Somerton, not far from Yarmouth. Hales died at Yarmouth in 1863, aged 43 (or 50, if one believes the inscription on the tombstone). In his prime he stood 7 ft 8 in. tall and weighed 452 lb. He measured 64 in. round the chest, 62 in. round the waist, and 21 in. round his calf. He came of a Patagonian family, and in early life was a seafarer, but became a showman and settled in London where the commercial possibilities of his figure were apparent. Both his mother and father were more than 6 ft tall while his four brothers averaged 6 ft 5 in. and his five sisters 6 ft 3 in. The tallest of the latter, Mary, was 7 ft 2 in. and accompanied him when he visited fairs and shows. She died at the early age of 20. After his career as a showman he took a public house in Sheffield, occasionally visiting his family in Norfolk, where he died on 22 November 1863.

Reedham

It was in the bar of the Lord Nelson I first met him, and if 'Spunk' Fisher was already an old man, it was not difficult to see written across his eyes the reason of his first name. As a boy he was very aggressive, and would have no fear in 'calling-out' a bigger and much older youngster than himself, hence the sobriquet of 'Spunk', 'Meanin' guts, sir,' as he would proudly inform you.

It is quite interesting to learn how the natives in these parts come by their nick-names. We hear of 'Sticky' Danvers, 'Fightin' Barker, 'Brawn' Davis, 'Strong' Webster, 'Cabber' Wakeson, 'Puncher' Adams, 'Powder' Filer, and so on. It will be remembered that the Danes, who almost colonised the littorals of these eastern counties, left their traditions to their descendants. The language of the people in Norfolk and Suffolk is interspersed with semi-Danish words, and their accent is like no other English dialect. Most of the ancient sea-kings of Denmark and their fighting men had names peculiar to their prowess or personal characteristics, such as 'Sea-King', 'Spray-Borne', 'The Serpent', and 'Sea-Giant', and so forth.

And so down through the ages the custom of nick-naming men has persisted, and in consequence most men have sobriquets by which they are often better known than by their surnames. Such names as I have mentioned, not forgetting 'Putty-nose', 'Slimey', 'Pudden-face', 'Dirty-neck' and 'Boss-eye', are usually bestowed when the men are but children, and they grow up with them and see little amiss in being called, as we might say 'out-of-place'. They more often than not represent some physical blemish or deficiency, and they carry them to the grave. And so Mr Fisher is better known as 'Spunk' than by his surname. Let me introduce you. Right! Shake hands. Now you know each other. Let's see, where were we? Oh, yes, in the saloon bar. How silly of me to forget.

Well, as I was saying, when you interrupted me, we replenished his empty quart mug, and sat down to pump him hard. He didn't take much pumping anyway, for two quarts of the Lord Nelson barley wine would loosen the dogs of war.

'Ghosts? Ghosts, did 'ee say? Whey, what are 'ee thinkin' on?

O' course there's ghosts here. We got the most wunnerful ghost in all Norfolk 'ere. Lots o' folks is scared to death over it, but them things don't frighten me, 'cause 'Spunk' Fisher's got nothin' to be frightened about. 'S only guilty consciences what's afraid o' ghosts, and old 'Spunk's' got a clean slate 'ee 'as, an' no mistake. Now don't keep interruptin' me, I'll tell 'ee all about the ghost o' Reedham, but first let me tell you – oh well, all right. 'E's bin goin' a long time, many long years, longer'n you nor me can go back. They do say as it's over a hundred year ago. Well, it was after the Romans come 'ere, and that's about the time, or just arter, say a hundred an' fifty year ago to be more exact.

'Now it so happened that one day a great Dane – I mean a Danish chief – was out doing a bit o' shooting, or whatever they used to do when catching birds – ah, hawking, that was it, amongst the Danish islands. He was out in a boat all by himself, he was, and a great storm came on, and before Mr Lothbrock – what a name! – could get home to Mrs Lothbrock, he was caught in the storm and carried out to sea. When the storm had gone down and he'd stopped being sick, he 'ad a look round and found himself on the coast o' Norfolk. He knew at once, cause 'e see the lightship on Scrobey, but I expect 'is Missis got a shock when he didn't come 'ome, and read about the awful storm in the next mornin's papers. I can see poor old Mrs Lothbrock down on the fish-quay, wringin' 'er apron, bitin' 'er 'ands, and endin' up as a comely widder-woman keepin' a little 'Anchor and 'Ope' on the strength of the insurance money.

'Well, to come back to Mr Lothbrock, when he found as he couldn't get back, 'cause it's a long row to Denmark – takes several hours by one o' them big packets out of Parkstone – and havin' lost 'is sails, and bein' all alone too, he decided to make up-river, not knowin' in the least what was in store for 'im, or if 'is biscuits and cheese would last out. You see, 'bor, in them days they 'adn't the scholarin' as we has today, and so he didn't know but what he might suddenly find hisself back in Denmark again, if he could keep on long enough.

'They do say that in them days there wasn't no Yarmouth, and the "Water" was a bit o' th' open sea, but it was always there in me old granfayther's time, 'cause I've heard 'n speak on it.

'Well, this Lothbrock feller came up as far as Reedham, here, where you be standin', and maybe come into this very house, but that I couldn't say for certain, and when he arrived there was a great doin's goin' on, 'cause the king was holdin' his court or something, what he always done at Reedham. You see, Reedham's not much to look at today, but in his time it was a very important place,

and when ole Lothbrock turned up, Edmund, what was King of the Saxons in East Anglia – that's all these parts round about here – in case you didn't know – well, he turned to his Lord High Executioner and Foot-Tickler in Chief, Lord Benjamin Berney, what was father-in-law to Josephine and grandpa to Bernadette, the little French "mawther", and says:

'"Hullo, Stickey! Breakers on the weather-bow."'

'To which the purple blooded aristocrat replied: "Sail ahoy!"'

'O' course, it was silly, we know that, 'cause poor old Lovebrick had lost the only one he had, but it was something like that anyway.

'"He ain't one of us," said Eddy, having a good look.'

'"He ain't," replied old Stickey, also bein' careful of his English.'

'"Go down and fetch 'im along and let's see what he wants. P'raps he's got some money on him."'

'And so when Mr Brothlick came alongside this very landin'-stage, he was received very welcome-like by old "Lord High", who would have spoke to him in Flemish only he hadn't got a cold, so he used his best Anglo-Saxon instead:

'"Who the – what the something are you?" he enquired, givin' him a hand ashore, and offerin' to carry his attachycase.'

'"Don't come that old stuff on me, and let go my bag," replied old Lovelock, mistakin' the good intention.'

'"Come up and meet Edmund King – I mean King Edmund. You are cold."'

'"Thanks, I am," said the sailor-man, "ruddy cold. I'll have a rum double and hot."'

'"I'll join you," answered Stickey, smackin' his lips, "and thanks very much."'

'So they come right in here, and stood on this very spot we'm standin' on now. Whilst they was argyfying as to who should pay, the King come in to see what they was such a long time about – at least, that's what he said. So they all had another round. When Eddy learned as he was from Denmark, o' course that meant another round, and then old Edmund, just to show how pleased he was, took his catapult and give him the acolade across the ear with it.

'Nowadays, o' course, it's different, you kneels down and the sword carves your saddle o' mutton, and when you gets up you're a knut, a knight or a knuke.

'So Sir Badluck became a member of Eddy's Court, and used to go everywhere with him. He was a great surprise in the hunting field, for he excelled everybody else. One day when they was in the roots, he loosed off a bunch from his crossbow right into the "brown", killin' five and woundin' the village copper who had left his beat to follow the royal bowers, archers – that's it.

' "You're some toxophilite," exclaimed the King, smotherin' his annoyance and smilin' out of his left ear.

'Now this was an unfortunate remark, 'cause one of his courtiers, Bern by name, overheard it, and always havin' fancied as he was the best what-the-King-called-the-other-feller, grew jealous, and one day put a bill-hook through Sir Blackduck's liver. When the King heard of this he was upset somethin' terrible, and sent for old man Bern, orderly-roomed him, and then instructed Stickey to provide a Saxon holiday.

'Poor old Bern. Sixty-six Saxons with saws, swords and sabres chased him all over the village, all up over old Sobey's fields to Buckenham and back again, but he got in first, and jumpin' into Sir Blackdog's fishin' punt, pushed off into mid-stream, spat a fearful ear-tearin' curse at old Eddy, and paddled like 'ell all the way to Denmark. When I say paddled, he stuck his pants up on a boat-hook, to be truthful, a storm came on, and afore he knew where he was he found hisself in the identical place where old Loveaduck had come from.

'When the people o' Denmark saw what they took to be old Sir Blackrock comin' home, they was so over-rejoiced that they ran right away and told the King, and people come runnin' from every part of the Kingdom to welcome him as he stepped ashore.

'You can picture their dismay when old Bern stepped ashore instead.

' "Who are you?" demanded the King, oh, very angry.

' "My name is Bern," he replied, steppin' on to the shingle and sprainin' his angle – I mean ankle.

' "What are you doin' in Blackdob's boat?"

' "Oh, I've just slipped across to tell you about him," he replied, rubbin' the wrong foot.

' "Indeed?" said the King. "Well, what is it?"

' "Well," answered Bern, quiverin' all over, "it's like this," and he proceeded to tell the most awful pack o' liards as ever fell from human lips, as the sayin' is. He told them that old Shivery-nob had landed in England and been massacred by King Edmund. Did you ever?

'Hinguor, King o' Denmark, couldn't believe it, so he sent word to his brother Hubba, whose other name was Bubble, and asked him to drop his Kingdom for a bit, and come across and have a yarn about poor old Lodrobski, which he done, and then they come to the conclusion that Bern was lyin'. So they called in their Lord High Torturer, who popped him on a grid-iron, to get the truth out of him, but Bern stuck to his guns. Then they put him on the rack to stretch his bones and his memory at the same time. But the old coward stuck it and to what he'd said, so they give him a commission from their War Office, made a general of him, and took him along with them and twenty thousand Danish-men to know the reason why.

'When they reached England they landed at Brancaster, and Bern led the way. After several scraps up North they reached Reedham and there was an awful battle. They took the swingbridge and then the church, and everything they could lay their hands on. Poor old Eddy, they caught him, too, disguised as a milkman sellin' peanuts and chewing-gum to their buscarles, but it wasn't good enough. They removed his crown, held a mock trial and sentenced him to death, with the result that they decapitartoed him first and then desiccated him arterwards. And that was the end of the Saxons in East Anglia.

'The ghost? Did you say what about the ghost? Oh, ah. Well, we've got one o' they all right. It is old man Bern. On every 21st August, that was the very day he was chased out o' Reedham, if you comes here about midnight and wait, you will see him come down the High Street here runnin' like a hare with a pack o' Saxons arter 'im with their spears and bows and arrers. His face is terrible to look at. All drawn and tightened with fear. They goes by here yellin' and shoutin', like a whirlwind sweepin' through the place.

'Our old vicar 'ere, not the present one, but two before him, actually saw Bern spring into the boat and sail down-stream, and he had no silly imagination about him. That night everyone keeps indoors, and locks and bolts all their windies and doors. You wouldn't get a person of Reedham out of his house that night, and every year it's the same. "Dirty" Spiker, who lives over at that red house with the green windies, was down fishin' last year on this particular night, just there where the river opens into the "Water", and he saw Bern go by in his boat and travellin' pretty fast, too, he was, in spite o' the fact that the night was still, and there wasn't a breath of air anywhere, and he wasn't rowin' or pushin', but just had some rags flapping from an upraised oar. He said the look on Bern's face was too terrible for anything, and he'll never forget it.

'But I wouldn't sit up for it, 'bor. It's unlucky to see a feller human bein' hunted to his death by a pack o' ruddy savages armed to the teeth, and swarmin' along like a gang o' murderin' cannibiles thirstin' for blood. No, 'bor, keep out of it, I says, and here's my best respects. Thank 'ee.'

Belaugh

When evening's shadows fall,
And gentle night, approaching,
Weaves new songs and tales of long ago,
O'er timbered crests with
Evening zephyrs filled.
And quietude steals slowly on,
In sweetest meditation.
Softly the vesper melody,
Resounding from the branches overhead,
As sweetly dies on lingering breath;
And feather babies 'wait the morning sun
That calls them from their lethargy
Of darkness, which
Closed their eyes and little hearts against
The chthonic fluvial progress
That, passing 'neath their resting-place,
Just faded into Dawn.

When Alys Lady Coverill penned these lines at Beulah, or Belagh, or
– as it is called today – Belaugh, in 1673, she had been listening to the
legend of the Bure from a woodman who worked in the great park
close by. In her memoirs she speaks of lingering by the 'slowly moving
waters at the foot of the hill, and being spiritually moved to higher
things.'

'I feel,' she writes, 'that somehow at this spotte that one is neare
very neare unto the other syde of lyfe. There is a sacred air about the
playce which comforteth me muchly, and allayes the petty annoyances of a busie lyfe.'

We are not told what a busy life for a 'ladye' of ease and luxury can
refer to, so are left guessing as to the probable cause of the 'petty
annoyances' which beset her.

It was through reading these memoirs that the author was
prompted to visit this beauty spot on the Bure, and investigate its
possibilities.

Belaugh is not far from Coltishall by road, although by river quite
a goodly distance, and, as is his custom, he did not go direct to
Belaugh to start his enquiries, for fear of starting the ball rolling in

an opposite direction, so he posted himself at the 'Rising Sun' at Coltishall, and in the guise of an artist, fraternised in the famous saloon-bar with all and sundry, and soon ingratiated himself in everybody's good books and their rural confidence in the usual way. Had the author tried to begin in Belaugh, the village would have shut up like a clam, and again, there is not a beer-house in the place, so it might not have been easy to unbridle the rustic informative tongue.

As it happens, many of the Belaugh populace find consolation and a certain aid to digestion in the short walk to the hostelry of the 'dawn', and having 'bought' myself in, so to speak, they fairly tumbled over themselves to tell me all about the annual phenomenon which takes place on the night of every 24 August, and causes everyone in the little village to bar and bolt their doors and windows, and under no circumstances to venture forth after sun-down. Even the little procession home from the Bacchanalian shrine in Coltishall begins well in time to enable each member to be in his house safely before the last flicker of a dying sun ceases to tinge the tree-tops and the tower of the village church.

Up at West Place, a fine old Carolean Manor, I was cordially invited to roam at will through the glorious park and paint whatever took my fancy, and one day Sir Geoffrey himself, out for a gun-stroll, invited me to join him at lunch at the house. After the meal he asked me if I would care to see the gallery, and together we wandered between rows of interesting Coverills, some in the armour of the king, others in that of the Church, whilst bewitching Lely and Sir Joshua ladies beamed at us in turn.

'That one,' said my host, indicating with his pipe a very fine looking person standing on the prow of a Saxon whelt, 'is said to be Olaf, Olaf Haraldsson, who came as an ally from Norway, and did so much to help England against the Danes. It was he, you know, to whom the people of London felt they owed so much that, in their gratitude, they dedicated several churches to him in London and elsewhere, and demanded his canonisation. St Olaf, or St Olave – well, that is supposed to be he, but you will notice that Sir Peter Van Dyke took for the portrait the fair lady Alys, another Coverill. Where is she? Ah, here we are. Now look at St Olaf and then look at Lady Alys. Same face.'

'Let me see,' I exclaimed, interrupting and playing my cards discreetly, 'I seem to have heard of her before somewhere. Now where could that be?'

'Ah,' he replied, delighted at my apparent knowledge, 'I expect you are referring to her memoirs. She was a poetaster, an aesthete, an – er – dreamer. Used to wander by the river and soliloquise and all that sort of nonsense. You know the kind.'

'But how interesting!' I answered, gradually coming to it, 'I wonder that she cared to go down there very much, all the same.'

'But why do you say that?' he enquired, with deepening interest.

'Well, somehow – oh, I don't know – but it makes me feel very strange when I'm near it. It is saddening. It is very, very eerie in places, and I wouldn't like to be down there after dark.'

'Well, now that's very strange you should have said that. Do you know that strange occurrences take place there every year?'

'You don't mean it?' I exclaimed, feeling an awful hypocrite. 'Tell me about it, will you?'

'Yes, if it won't disturb you, and cause you to leave us.'

'Why should it?' I asked.

'Well, it so happens that today is 24 August, and this is the day, or rather the very night.' I tried to register surprise.

'Would it be possible to see it – whatever it is that happens?'

'So you are interested, eh? Well, so am I. Shall we go down together? I've seen it before, and it certainly is most interesting. You dine here tonight, just as you are – the ladies are away – and later on we'll stroll down and push the punt a little way up past the village. There'll be no one about. They'll all be well under their bed-clothes tonight, and we'll have the river to ourselves.'

After dinner that night we went into the capacious library and smoked, and about ten o'clock we put on heavy, warm travelling coats and repaired to the river. We untied the punt and soon were paddling towards Belaugh. The river winds a good deal just here, and it took us quite a while to reach the spot my host suggested. As we came to the village it was all tucked up and asleep, and not a light in a window was to be seen.

The little garden with the summer-house and quay, where I had seen a pretty little girl playing earlier in the day with a large dog, was deserted, and the boat-builder's sheds stood out in the clear evening light, deserted also. Silently we drifted by, and the night was still and quiet, the fireflies in the hedges vieing with the stars overhead, sometimes looking like water reflections of the stellar iridescence above, in the dark shadows at the side of the river.

The sky in the west reminded me of the song *Sink, Red Sun*, and the blazing red of its final display splashed across the firmament with wondrous beauty. What a sunset! What a ravishing blaze of colour! Sir Geoffrey interrupted my musings.

'Ah – you never see a sky like that except on 24 August. Always the same. I have noted it since I was a boy, and the old gardener told me. It is part of the tradition.'

We were now some distance past the church, at least where the tower mirrors itself in the Bure, and had paddled into the side and tied up to an overhanging branch. Here we lay quite still, watching the smoke from our pipes curling up in the still night air. Then my host spoke in a very soft whisper:

'Presently, when the church strikes the quarter, keep a good look-out and watch that little path on the other side. She always comes down that way and wanders along in this direction.'

We waited patiently, scarce daring to move lest we might make some noise and so disturb the 'conditions'. Have you ever waited full of expectation, dear reader, for the great something that seemed never to come? Moments drag on like hours, and one's patience becomes almost exhausted. I was in a very tucked-up and cramped position, my legs wanted to stretch, and my arms to reach out and splash the water. Anything was better than this awful suspense. Then suddenly the church clock chimed the quarter, and I strained my eyes for all they were worth in the direction I had been told.

My host then leaned across and whispered, 'Do you feel that icy-cold breeze fanning you all over.' I most certainly did.

'Look,' he exclaimed under his breath, 'look, she's coming.' I looked again.

'Where?' I asked.

Then pointing with his finger, I followed it with my eyes, and there, coming down the path from the churchyard, was a tall glow of light. It moved very slowly, but did not illuminate anything around it. One could not make out any form because it was not near enough, but as it came slowly nearer, it appeared to become brighter. Arriving at the riverside it paused, and I was able to gauge its height and breadth, and I should say it was about the proportions of a slender person, say five-feet-six or seven. From where we were it was merely an erect form of light.

My back shivered, and my teeth clenched, as a cold sweat broke out all over my face. But I was not to be daunted, if my old heart did start pounding away at my ribs. We had prepared ourselves for this experience by carefully abstaining from any intoxicating liquor earlier in the evening, or we might have attributed what we were witnessing to hallucinations due to an unbalanced alcoholic influence. We were as sober and aware as we are at this moment, and our eyes were riveted on this extraordinary phenomenon. I can quite understand the villagers taking all the precautions they do on this annual occasion. I personally was divided in my emotion. One side of me rather envied them, if anything, whilst another side of me would not have missed this event for anything.

Presently the form took shape, and slowly out of it there developed a beautiful girl clad in a white high-waisted frock which reached the ground, and the entire human form seemed to be illuminated from within. It cast no light around, but just was luminescent within itself to its sharpest outline. She stood with a book in her left hand, and with her right she shaded her eyes as she gazed up the river into the darkness beneath the trees. Then she called softly in the direction she was looking, 'O . . . laf! O . . . laf!'

There was a small plaintive ring in her tiny voice, a cry from a tired soul, tired with waiting. It echoed away up the stream out of hearing, and presently it returned and we heard it in our direction.

'O . . . laf! O . . . laf!' she called again, more sweetly than ever, and then she slowly turned, and walking along the little path on the bank, read from her book. As she approached it was easy to see how beautiful she really was, her flaxen hair falling in two long 'Marguerite' plaits in front of her. Her cheeks were like a child's, spotless and clear, and her dark blue eyes contrasted with her rich blonde colouring. Her walk was almost gliding, and when she stopped almost in front of us, my eyes were ravished with her loveliness, and I could recognise her at a glance as she whom the court painter had portrayed on his canvas, and which was now hanging in the gallery at the Manor.

As she stood there it was difficult to believe that she, this beautiful living human creature, had come down from the cold vaults above where she had lain dead for nigh three hundred years. Here she was, a real, living entity in apparently real and tangible flesh and blood, and yet destined to return in a short while to the funerary abode from which she had come. One was seized with a desire to hold her so that she should not go back. She was not dead, she was as alive as you or I, and yet destiny decreed that to that inhospitable, responseless tomb she must return, and, assuming her death-robes, become a corpse once more.

What it was that held me back I do not know, but although the impulse to jump out of the boat and go to her was on me, I could not move. I was terrified, filled with wonder, gratified, and yet disappointed all at the same time. Scientists tell us we cannot feel two pains, think two thoughts, or experience more than one emotion at the same moment, but don't you believe it. I experienced all four emotions at one and the same instant.

Closing her book, Lady Alys gazed up-stream once more into the darkness, and called again. Then, suddenly, she clasped her hands on her breast in ecstasy, her face lighted up with smiles, her rich dark velvety eyes danced with joyous anticipation, and she leaned forward and stretched out her arms as though she could see him coming. And he was.

From a long way up-river there came as it were the sounds of sweet music and the singing as of many voices, all sweetly harmonised, and gradually it came nearer. My host leaned over and whispered: 'Don't take your eyes off that bit of the river.'

Slowly out of the darkness I was able to descry a huge blunt-nosed vessel like a Norseman's ship coming down stream. She had many people on board, and was followed by several similar vessels all laden with flowers, and with choirs in white, singing. In the bow of the first stood a man in the white robes of a Saxon king, illuminated, like Lady Alys, from within. On his head he wore a narrow golden crown, and his long fair hair curled into his neck. As he came closer I could see him quite clearly, his two hands resting on the cruciform hilt of a two-handed sword against his breast, with the point downwards between his feet.

As soon as his eyes fell on hers, he dropped on one knee, and held out his arms in loving desire to come to him, but the clock in the belfry struck the midnight hour, and all she could do was to throw him a passionate kiss, and hurry back the way she had come along the little path on the bank, and up the steep slope to the church.

Olaf's face was the living double of Lady Alys, and was so striking it caused me to gasp.

He followed her lovingly with his eyes until she had passed out of sight, then he stepped back into the middle of the boat, and laid himself down on his back with his sword still in the same position, as though he were lying-in-state, surrounded by the flowers, the voices continued their song of prayer, and as the last boat of this silent cortège glided by and disappeared with the others downstream into the dimness of nocturnal oblivion, we were bathed in a holy silence that was incapable of being violated.

And so ended a most uncanny experience which is open to anybody who wishes it, and one which I would not have missed for anything in the world. It gives one plenty of food for reflection, and opens up many channels of conjecture.

I did not know the story beforehand, my host having thought it more politic to let me witness the manifestation first, if it was to be granted to me to see it, and hear the story afterwards.

The suggestion that I did not see it at all, but that it was a mental projection on his part into my mental spheres would be infinitely more wonderful by a long chalk, than that the whole episode did actually take place. And, finally, how is it that so many scores of other people besides me have witnessed it as well?

Horsey Mere

Com with me to Happie-Towne
Where lyfe is bryte and gaye,
And little children playe all daye
And never knowe a frowne.
Oh, com with me and joyne them
In theyre gladde joyous thronge,
Oh, com oute here
To Horseye Mere
And synge the children's songe!
Lines from 'The Children's Paradise' – Anon. (*c.* 1460)

So sang the fifteenth-century poet who hid his identity 'neath the shield of anonymity. And of Horsey Mere, too, which rather indicates this delectable spot was recognised even in those days. The lines are very like Smalldridge's, and yet the metre resembles Campion, and as they both were East Anglians it could probably be either.

The author was scanning some old books in the large library at Weston Thurtyss one rainy day last year when he came across the stanza above and, determined to make a note of it, copied it out for future reference. Later in the year he found himself cruising in the neighbourhood of Potter Heigham, and so made a point of investigating this piece of water and gleaning as much information as possible concerning its history and local traditions.

In analysing the name we find that the last syllable 'ey' may have two derivations. One is the contraction of 'eyott', or Saxon for 'island', a small islet in a river (*Times' Century Dictionary*) and also an abbreviation on the other hand of the word 'Hythe' meaning a landing-place, such as obtained in Puttenhythe, or as we know it today, Putney. In the days of the Romans, Horsea Island stood in what would have been the estuary of the Thurne, or an arm of the sea – Oceanus Germanicus – which washed through to meet the Bure, and merging into the Garienis Ostium made an island of the East and West Fleggs.

At Potter I managed to fraternise with several of the local natives, and they all shook their heads and knew nothing of interest concerning this delicious Mere. One very old 'bor did ask me had I never heard of its 'hantings', when the others tried to persuade him to 'dry up'. He was a dear old man and I managed to engage him for a little 'fishing' the following day, and he procured for me a fourteen-foot dinghy with a convulsive coffee-pot in it, that chugged and chugged us up Heigham Sound, through the Meadow Dike and on to Horsey Mere.

Our entry I shall never forget. It was a priceless day – 13 June invariably is – and a perfect cerulean sky lay overhead without fleck or shadow, and old man 'Sol' blazed down upon us like a furnace. Emerging from the Dike we glided around the Mere, which is quite small, and scarred its mirror surface with our wake. At the far end is a small islet rather overgrown with reeds, and on looking back it was not at all easy to make out the spot where we had come in, as the banks of this hallowed water are hidden by reeds. It was so peaceful and quiet, it seemed a crime to break in upon its calm serenity, and we were the only people on the Broad.

'Did you say this place is haunted?' I enquired, coming quickly to the point, and not giving him time to draw back, added 'Yes?'

For answer he nodded his old head and looked me straight in the eye.

'Do tell me about it, 'bor. There's a good fellow.' I went on.

'But you wouldn't b'lieve it, 'bor,' he said, half smiling, and tapping out his old clay on the gunwale.

'Believe it, man? Of course I'd believe it if you do. Let's hear about it.'

'Did y'ever hear o' the Row-mans, 'bor?' he enquired, doubtfully and hesitant. I answered him I had.

'Well it dates back to they. In them days when a little child died they brought 'im out 'ere and weightin' the little body, they lowered it down to the bottom of this pool. It's the spirits o' them childer what hants this place, and this very night is "Childer's Night", when all their little bodies come to life again for an hour and sing and play just as they did in the flesh.' He thought he noted some expression of incredulity in my face, and added:

'Ah, I thought as you wouldn't. I thought as you wouldn't, but it's true, true it is 'bor.'

I hastened to reassure him and enquired whether he had ever seen or heard them.

'Twice, 'bor. Once when a hobbildy (young man) and again five years agone,' and then he proceeded to recount to me a most fascinating story, which was borne out by my own experience that very night.

We went ashore and visited the inn at the little village, and there I was fortunate enough to meet a man who is an Antiquary, and from him I learned identically the same history of the Broad. We became such immediate friends that he offered to join us in our fishing that night, and by 9.30 p.m. was back at the inn. We took a stack of sandwiches, some excellent rock-cakes, the product of the inn's own kitchen, pushed off in the dinghy, and moored on the south-east side of the mere. At the suggestion of fishing, old 'granfer' expressed a hope 'as we wouldn't on no account begin afore one o'clock o' th' mornin'.' His reasons were easy to divine and we respected them, so we lay back in the boat and feasted our eyes on the canopy of heaven, which was specially clear, the stars standing out with extraordinary sharpness and relief.

The time passed amusingly enough, what with yarning and exchanging ideas on metaphysical phenomena, and we were very careful to refrain from any stimulating liquor, although we had come well-equipped in this respect.

About 11.30 p.m. the sky began to grow a little dim, and by 11.45 p.m. it was quite dark, and we extinguished our lantern.

Then began the most interesting syndrome of events. A soft

gentle zephyr stirred the reeds and the fireflies began to light up one at a time, at different spots, and become very bright. On the ruffled breathings of the air came the distant, ever so distant, sounds of the sweetest music imaginable. It was music, but not as the human ear is accustomed to hear it. It was minute and clear, and harmonised beyond the wildest dreams of human ecstasy. The reeds by now were aglow with a myriad tiny lamps and their light upon the mirror surface of the water was reflected in a thousand directions. And now it was noticeable that the circle of lights was rising, but curiously enough extending downwards, and on further examination it was apparent that it was not that they were rising, but that the water in the lake itself was sinking, and our little craft was being left suspended in mid-air. All of which sounds incredible, but read on.

At last the water had completely gone, and in its place was a beautiful green sward with flower-beds and borders teeming with priceless blooms. It was quite easy to see because of the wall of light all round, for the reeds now extended down some thirty feet below us. Then the music grew, and presently we could hear a miniature military orchestra below and somewhere at the side, and presently, as it swelled, there was a fanfare of tiny trumpets, the reeds parted, and in came a naked host of the prettiest children, dancing and clapping their hands in sheer delight. Following them came a large Nubian lion with the sweetest little Titania astride him. Her long flowing flaxen hair fell about her little undraped body like the finest gossamer with the dew on it. Round her head was a circlet of gold with seven spires, and from the tip of each twinkled a brilliant little star.

Following her came more lions and tigers and leopards, and thousands, not hundreds, of little children. In the matter of raiment there was no attempt at 'cover', for it was not necessary. No evil or unkind thought could find existence amidst such simple charm and purity. They were all so happy and gay, so completely abandoned in their joy and pleasure, that the night air rang with their merry laughter, and as they romped and played with the fearsome looking beasts they knew that they would not hurt them. They pranced to the drums and carolled like lambs, throwing themselves into their enjoyment whole-heartedly, running here and rushing there, and playing to their hearts' content.

A more beautiful sight my eyes had never witnessed, and no more striking evidence could confirm the hereafter and the great love of the Creator for his tiny children, the men and women who might have been, but instead were called to the 'Children's Paradise'.

Then, as suddenly, there appeared a brilliant, shining light in their midst, more blinding than any electric arc, and casting its rays all round, so that every nook and cranny was lighted up. The little children's bodies became almost iridescent as this wonderful light fell upon them, and then we saw them all run wildly towards it.

In a moment the dazzling glare had modified and there stood in its midst the most wonderful man human eye has ever seen. His flowing simple white robes fell about him to his feet, and his hair, which was long and slightly dark auburn, just fell about his neck and shoulders. He was holding out his hands, and smiling at them with a marvellous expression of love upon his face. They clung on to him and danced around him with an abandon that was beautiful to see, and then, bending down, he picked up a tiny girl and boy in each arm, and as he lifted them up they twined their little bare and chubby arms about his neck. He was so pleased, and laughed with joy at being with them in their play, and as he did so, he showed the most perfect teeth I have ever seen, white as snow. He was talking to them, but we could not make out what he said, and as he spoke they became absolutely silent and listened, and when he had finished they simply burst with delight and danced and sang wildly around him. That he was a great favourite with them went without saying; they just worshipped him, whoever he was. Then he strolled about amongst them, patting little heads here, stopping to caress there, ruffling their curls with his long white fingers, laughing and just loving being with them. He patted the beasts who licked his hands, and one huge Bengal man-eater stood on its hind-legs and placed its paws on his shoulders and tried to lick his face. He patted it gently and spoke to it, and it got down and licked his feet.

What a wonderful sight it was. And then he looked up, as we thought, at us, and smiled. It was a moment I shall never forget. To attempt to describe the emotion that thrilled me is beyond the compass of words, or even music, and must be experienced to be appreciated. No idle phraseology could do justice to it. It was as though a great blessing had been poured into the very depths of one's soul, and that's as far as human understanding in its limitless and finiteness can go. Then he stooped down and picked up a fragile little girl and loved her up, her pale little body contrasting with his own skin, and as she sat over his forearm with her little shock of curls nestling into his neck, we were able to make out the stigmata in His hands.

It was at that moment we realised it all. This was indeed the Children's Paradise, and we had been vouchsafed a peep into it.

Slowly the lights grew dim, and all this display of happiness gradually faded out, the music becoming further and further distant until it died right away, the waters gradually returned, and as they rose so the little lamps at the side went out. In a few minutes the dinghy was once more afloat, the fairies had dimmed their firefly lamps, the sky had cleared and the stars shone out brighter than ever. We looked at each other but could not speak. What mundane thought was there that was worth talking about.

The old man re-lighted the lantern, but we had no desire to fish, so we undid the sandwiches and brought out the flask.

Townshend in his *Strange Happenings*, published in 1692 mentions this wonderful phenomenon, but his records evidently came through hearsay, for he does not state that he actually witnessed them, but it does go far to show that as long ago as his day this magnificent manifestation was known.

It has also been mentioned by Mr Justice Truby, in the Transactions of the East Anglian Archæological Society in December 1709, wherein he states that 'these mysterious manifestations are common knowledge to the folke of the country-side in these partes, but they do not openly speak of them, for feare of frightening their children, and also to preserve muchly the sanctity of the "Children's Mere".' *Quien Sabe?*

Ormesby

When in the British Museum one day, I happened to come across in a book on Norfolk a gruesome reference to Ormesby Broad, and read it again and again. It began with the following stanza:

> When ye wynde's syngynge in ye roshes,
> And ye moone's behinde ye clowde,
> Go, haste ye from ye waters of Norsemansburough,
> Beware ye ides of Maye and girte ye loynes
> With prayer, ye fastynges and ye almes.
> King Deathe he stalkes abroade,
> But feare ye not if
> Thou'rt prepared to mete thy Godde.

It so impressed me that I decided to go down to 'Norsemansborough', and learn what there was to be seen or known about this delectable mere and its immediate vicinity. Accordingly I found myself in due course in Norfolk, and making discreet inquiries in every direction. In the little village of Ormesby it was not easy to get the native 'willing and giving', for at the mention of anything in the nature of a legend they closed down like the lid of a box. At the little rustic 'Pig and Face-ache', near the northerly end of the Broad, I did find a dear old gaffer who 'could tell a lot o' things if 'e'd a mind to', so I replenished his empty tankard and laid my ground bait.

'It's very quiet round here, isn't it?' I began, commencing very cautiously.

''Ess, 'bor,' he replied good-naturedly, 'too quiet for some on 'em, I'm thinkin'. What with all this dancin', and boys and gals doin' as they loikes, why, bless me, I can't make out what's comin' to 'em all, I can't.'

'Ah,' I butted in interestedly, 'now that's what I call good sense. When they're dead and gone and their spirits come back, they'll see all the results of their folly.'

''Bor,' said the old man, putting down his mug, and looking hard at me, 'you'm right. Oh, you'm right enough.'

'Well,' I went on, 'we do come back sometimes, don't we?'

'And you believe that, too?' he enquired, shifting nervously in his chair.

'Most certainly I do. I believe in ghosts and hauntings and all those things, because I have seen and heard them for myself.'

'Ah,' he grunted self-convincingly, 'there be one as you 'aven't seen, nor 'eard tell of, for that matter, I'm sartin.'

'I know. You're referring to the one at Ormesby Broad.'

'You do know about it then,' he replied, gazing with surprise at me. 'What 'ave you 'eard?'

'Well, I'll tell you. Wait a moment. You tell me your version, and then I'll see if mine is correct. Have some more beer.' The quart being re-filled, I leaned forward and said quietly:

'Now, tell me what you were going to.' The old man, completely whisked off his balance, fell to my 'decoy', and this is the story he told me. As on a former occasion, I am not recounting it in the dialect. I could not do justice to it, so beg your acceptance of it in my lingo and not his.

Many years ago there was a very rich miller who had a lovely daughter, and, curious to relate, they 'lived beside the mill'. Now the fair Alyson – that was her name, but she was usually known to most as Alys – was so beautiful that people used to come from quite long distances to see her, and one day, it is said, that an esquire arrived all the way from Aberdeen, wherever that may be, not so much to be staggered by her ravishing beauty as to spy out the land, and endeavour to elicit the extent of the 'old man's' resources; in other words, to find out if he did marry the girl, what kind of dowry she could expect from her father, and at his decease, how much would she be worth. There are some people who think of everything, and always in terms of money. They are the people who call us Sassenachs.

Well, one day the 'old man' took his winsome daughter aside, and said:

'Alys, my dear, you'm no longer a li' chiel, but a grown woman, and therefore old enough to begin thinkin' seriously about a husband.' Had he gone steady, and said 'sweetheart', instead of 'husband', leaving that to follow in due course, he would not have made such a mess of his own life and his daughter's as he did.

Now it so happened that he was tired of milling, and it had occurred to him that if he could get a good price for his mill, perhaps six times what he gave for it, and marry off his girl to some wealthy person, he could retire from his labours, and manage to pull along comfortably on his own capital, and the allowance he would reasonably expect from his wealthy son-in-law.

And so when the great 'Mac' from over yonder arrived and called upon him, he was so excited he could scarce contain himself, and started running around, washing his hands with imaginary soap, and saying stupid things in his excitement. The bra' Hielander eyed him critically, and scratched his head in grave doubt as to the exact condition of the old man's brain, and on questioning the fair Alys, was informed it was really nothing, that her father often 'took on' like that, and that he was to take no notice of anything he might say or dò. It would have been one thing to make such a remark to a heathen Chinee, but to say it to a bra' Scottie was another. He packed up, but before leaving he exclaimed, 'I like the gur-rl, but you, ye old skinflint, may the devil seize ye and your old mill, too!'

That there had been a grievous wordy warfare between them their attitude towards one another left no room for doubt, and any misgivings one might have had on the matter were immediately set at rest by the miller replying:

'May hell claim ye, the mawther (young girl) and the mill, for all your damned trickery. If the "old man" was here now I'd give him my soul to take you away.'

Strong and unguarded language is ever dangerous, even under the mildest conditions, and no sooner had he let slip the fatal remark than an elderly gentleman whom they had not noticed standing close by, suddenly turned, and gripping him by the hand, exclaimed, 'Done!' Or words to that effect.

Before one could say 'knife', the miller, his daughter and their Scotian visitor were transported to inside the mill, which now went up in flames and roared like a furnace.

This takes place every year as regularly as day follows night, and as sure as 15 May comes round so this happening repeats itself, as it has done for the last three hundred years or more.

I filled his mug again, but didn't believe a word of his story, which he seemed to fathom, and I fear it hurt him.

Accordingly, the following year I went down to Ormesby Broad again, and this time on 15 May – notice, the Ides of May, eight days after the Nones, which in May happens on the 7th – and I had with me the Reverend Owen Anwyl Davies, D.D., Sir Beaufort Craig, the eminent physicist, Dr Gordon Beacher, of the Institute of Technology, South Kensington, and Cameron Lacey, D.Sc., F.R.S., the well-known seismologist and metaphysician.

You can see from these names that my company was well-chosen, firstly on account of their being the four greatest authorities in the realm of science, and whose dicta would stand for acceptance before anybody else's, seeing that they were men who were capable of sifting evidence and appreciating what was evidential and what was not. And, secondly, because all four were staunch total-abstainers.

We brought an 'outboard skimmer' and made fast alongside where the mill stands on the spit or knuckle of land, which juts out into the Broad just south of the Mill Hill coverts, and looking right down the whole length of the water. It was an admirable position for observation, and we brought with us a stack of sandwiches, fruit, and hot coffee in vacuum flasks.

Beacher, although his deep interest in metaphysics had impelled him to come, was obviously prepared to see nothing at all. The learned doctor of divinity was not quite sure that he was not giving 'cover' to the powers of evil by being present, whilst Sir Beaufort was inordinately quiet and prepared for anything. Cameron Lacy preserved a very definite and defiant attitude, not easily shaken, and was one who was honest enough anyway to let every man believe what he had seen.

I deem it only fair to the reader and ourselves to explain the various mental attitudes of those present, lest some critical person may say that what we witnessed was what we desired to, which after all, though in a different sense, was perfectly true, because we did actually travel all that distance in order to see anything that turned up. For myself, well, those who know me are satisfied that I am of sound mind, hypercritical to a degree in all that appertains to the 'other side', and have spent thirty years in the study of metaphysics at home and abroad, and in exposing fraudulent mediums. (A word en passant – it is the disclosure of imposture that feeds the desire for truth, and if there were no truth there could be no falsehood, hence a fraudulent medium unwittingly serves to prove the existence of the spiritual world by his lying ability to demonstrate.)

It must have been about 10.30 p.m. when we arrived, and after a quiet cigarette, we stretched ourselves on the cushions and waited. The clouds were racing across the sky and the night was mild and balmy, the gentle breeze filling the sails and turning the great mill was the only other sign of movement. The crested grebe, the heron, dabchick and moorhen had long since tucked themselves up for the night, and it seemed as though the presence of five men in a boat, the only things with their eyes open possibly for miles, was quite out of place here on an evening like this. But here we were, and we all looked at each other, and the same thought occurred to us all.

Presently a church clock struck half-past eleven, and still we waited. Again that church clock struck, and this time the witching time of night, when graveyards yawn and hell breathes out contagion to the world. And still nothing happened. The quarter-past the hour, and then the half struck, and it looked as though we were to be disappointed, even the old mill turning on its never-ending task seemed to look down on us from a great height with its tongue in its cheek. The quarter-to, and then one o'clock struck and still nothing happened.

Beacher leaned across and said under his breath. 'You had the date right?'

I assured him I had, and then suddenly the breeze dropped, cold chills ran down our spines, we looked quickly at each other and then we saw something dark outline itself on the bank. It appeared to have crawled up out of the water, and on looking closely we saw the human outlines of three people, apparently in altercation. Then suddenly they all turned, apparently saw us, and ran into the mill. The windows lighted up, and we waited and waited, but nothing seemed to happen. What puzzled us was how long those three people had been lurking near our boat on the bank before they showed themselves.

Sir Cameron said it was impossible for an ordinary person to keep still for so long and not be noticed. Beacher said they were some villagers who thought they would have a lark with us. Sir Beaufort saw no reason why they should have been mortal at all. Then I enquired if they weren't mortal what did they want with a light in the mill, and why their mysterious, secretive behaviour. Lacey said we hadn't seen them at all, and when we pointed out the lights in the mill, swore they had been there all the time. (Some people are really very trying.) I fear he nettled me somewhat, and I blurted out:

'Perhaps you'll tell us there is no mill there, and that we're not here at all.'

'I'm so sorry,' he pleaded, realising he had unwittingly trespassed on our intelligence. 'I ought not to have said that,' he went on. 'Yes, the mill's there, and we're here, too, though what for, well—— God! Did you here that?' He started, and so did we, and although I couldn't see him very well in the dark, I'll bet he went deathly pale.

Again a piercing scream came from the mill, and then another. Craig was about to spring out of the boat and make for the door, when suddenly a huge flame licked out of a lower window and caught the sails. With a whistle it spread in a flash from arm to arm, and the revolving wheel of flame made a picture none of us will ever forget. The flames were now leaping out of all the windows, and flicking upwards, reddening the sky and illuminating everything as clear as day for some distance around. After a few more moments the whole mill was a living, growling conflagration, hurling into the illumined sky streams of sparks which fell in showers all around.

Huge pieces of blazing wood were flung high into the air and fell with sickening thuds and splutterings into the reeds and water around us. Every time a flying fragment of incandescence struck the water it seemed to burst like high explosive, and fling itself into the air again in a column of steam. Several larger pieces continued to glow in the reeds for quite a while, but eventually the damp blanketed them, and they fizzled out.

The mill was now a roaring, angry volcano, and the roof having fallen in, a huge blast furnace was belching its fury into the sky, and the old arms still kept turning slowly, falling to pieces and breaking up on the ground in little bursts of sparks. No one appeared to have come from the villages to attempt to save the building, and the people who had run into the mill were not anywhere about, but we reckoned they had evacuated it when the fire broke out, and in all probability had raced off for help.

Then suddenly the air was rent once more by a piercing scream, clear above the roaring blaze, and which must have been audible for miles, and at the same moment a girl appeared at the top window amidst the flames.

What was to be done? She was quite helpless, and we sprang ashore, all five of us, prepared to race up and try anyway to do something, when, as suddenly, she flung herself, a sheet of living flame, out into space. As she fell, a huge sheet of red flame came down out of the darkness, and enveloping her, bore her away, and we were able to recognise in the second flame the form of a huge devil. The two men appeared in turn alive with flame – I had no idea the human body was so inflammable – and flinging themselves out of the window, were immediately caught up by two more devils of gigantic size, whose bodies were also of fire, and carried away into the darkness of the night.

Slowly the mill fell in, its sides collapsing, and sheets of flame a hundred feet or more in height, licking up as each floor gave way. The noise of the crackling and spitting was almost deafening, but the heat was terriffic. Our faces and hands were scorched and stiff.

The Broad reflected this awful fire until it looked like a sea in Hell itself. The smell of burnt flour, sacking and oil nearly made us ill, but it was the brimstone that was coupled with it that stung our eyes so, and made them so painful.

At long last it died down, and when all danger was past we closed our note-books, and crawled into our sleeping-bags.

The following morning, on waking, we gazed at each other in horror. Our faces were black and our eyebrows and lashes and the uncovered parts of our hair were all scorched away, whilst Sir Beaufort's eyes were very inflamed from the heat. We bathed our faces in the mere and then went ashore to view the remains of the ill-fated mill. You can imagine the shock we received on finding not a trace of the mill or the slightest sign of where it had stood.

As we stood inspecting the ground very closely, an early morning ploughman going to his work called out: 'Larst anythin', 'bor?' And then, with a self-satisfied grunt and a laugh, ambled on his way. He knew.

Ludham

Awaye acrost faire Ludham's Playne, the wilde Nordie bande
Comes gallopynge in head-longe stryde to seize the pasture lande,
From far and neare the cattel dryve, and herd theme rite awaye.
Stand bye, ye men of Anglia and halte theyre cruel foraye;
Prepare thy swordes and digge thee dykes
And fill the deetches fulle of pykes.
Stande bye, North-folke of Anglia
And garde thy homes and praye!
William Boulter. *Songs of East Anglia*, AD 1472 (*c.*)

These lines of the fifteenth-century poet are very interesting in that
they apply today as well as they did in the early Briton's time, if
perhaps in a different manner. There can be no question that in the
early history of this part of the country raiders from overseas were
quite the order of the day, and it behoved the natives of East Anglia
to keep a constant watch for the 'Nordic bands' who found a place
so convenient and suitable to plunder. Cattle driving, pillage and
arson were hobbies with these northern marauders, and it was not
until the Saxons came and discovered what a much better place it
was to live in than their own, that these sudden attacks became less
frequent, and the counties of Norfolk, Suffolk and Essex were able
to enjoy their peaceful agricultural industries and preserve the
sanctity of home life. But even down to this year of grace the folk-
songs of the indigenes remind us of those undesirable times, and the
native traditions yet hold that the raiders still come once a year at
least, and always by night, to rob them and despoil them of the
hard-earned rewards of their honest toil.

At Ludham Bridge three years ago, whilst waiting for water and
stores, I happened to strike-up a conversation with an antiquary
who, though he had only met me for a few minutes, gave me a
detailed information regarding these forays at night, and which
always took place on 2 April. This date is a little early for most
members of the sailing world, and perhaps that is why so few people
make a point of attempting to be present on one of these hectic
occasions. The following year I had to go myself. The prospect of a

super-normal manifestation was too attractive for me to ignore, and accordingly, on the evening of the aforementioned date, I was moored alongside the bank at Ludham Bridge, full of anticipation, perhaps risibly critical, but above all determined to see anything that could make itself visible.

I always feel about these things that one should never be too ready to condemn them as absurdities or stupid vagaries of a mind disordered, but to try and appreciate them from the simplest standpoint possible, and as far as is in one's power to endeavour to place oneself in the same mind as those who have already witnessed these things, and try hard to see what can be seen from the same angle. I am convinced that the negative mind achieves nothing, and the moment it sets out upon its 'quest', places an unmistakable barrier between desire and achievement. The person who is ever ready to scout the supernormal is the one person who never does and never will see anything, not, as he may flatter his vanity by thinking that nothing can 'get past him', but through sheer ignorance of trying to adapt his three-dimensional empiricism to things which are beyond science as we know it. That same unhappy man is he who would measure thought with a foot-rule.

Let's see. Where were we? Oh, yes, at Ludham Bridge.

Well, 'Bert', the cabin-boy, 'Bill', the winch-hand, the mate and I, trimmed the ship, and prepared for an interesting vigil. About 10 p.m. some dense clouds blew away, the stars came out, and there was a prospect of a little moon if the wind permitted. There were plenty of local craft around, but few people, which was rather surprising for such a beautiful spot, but possibly the great army of invasion had not deemed it wise to venture forth in flannels and cricket shirt so early in the year. Still, those who do start early in the season most certainly see the Broads at their best, and perhaps, as the nocturnal attractions become better known, we shall find this deficiency rectify itself.

Well-wrapt in rug and blanket, our crew spread itself on the deck and talked of other adventures, some more venturesome than others, which had fallen to our experience in collecting so many of these chronicles. From where we were we had an uninterrupted view of the extensive marsh and meadow-land to the east of Ludham Bridge, whilst behind us and to the west, more flats stretched away into the distance of the night. A wherry was coming down-river and her large black sail stood out well against the silver-blue of the evening sky. It was most pleasant, mild, and still, only a night-jar now and again breaking the quiet – at least, Bert said it was a night-jar, so I take it as correct – occasionally a screech owl broke forth with his 'tweet-too-woo-oo', and the river glided gently by, winding its way to the open sea, without a ripple, without a sound.

Although so perfect a night, it was just right for ghosts and stories of hair-raising adventures, the kind of night when anything could come down on the wind, or suddenly appear before one, when hob-goblins could assemble and chatter like death-hawks, or hurlo-thrumbos stalk abroad, whilst gorgons, mormoes and ogres could vie with raw-heads and bloody-bones, and wrangle for the offal from charnel-houses. Ee-Yi-Yi!

Somehow or other we started talking about the old Luffincot Rectory, whose story, by the way, would freeze the flame of a lighted candle, when suddenly 'Bill' gave a great start, for on looking around, she saw a large harmless cow chewing the cud and eyeing us all as though we had no right to be there. We had not noticed any cattle in the meadow before, but on looking around we could now make out quite easily a fair-sized herd grazing in the peaceful quietude of the mead.

An atmosphere of apprehensive tranquillity had environed everything during this transition stage from twilight into darkness, and the mention of anything ethereal or spiritual had an uncanny ring about it, whilst the mere suggestion of anything metaphysical sent our nerves a-tingling. A chilly zephyr came across the river and our limbs quivered, but the mate noticed that the smoke from our pipes was not deflected. This eerie feeling of uncertainty was accompanied by a tremulous sensation down the back as of cold water trickling down the spine. We all felt it and gave a little shiver. We were puzzled to understand why we should feel like this.

'Bill' said it was the same feeling that she had when she was once on a bus, and an old gentleman in front of her discovered he had no money, and she asked him to let her pay his fare for him. He thanked her, the conductor took the coppers, gave him his ticket, and when 'Bill' the next moment looked up, the old man had vanished. She mentioned it to the conductor and whilst she was telling him, the real conductor came down from collecting the fares upstairs, and the one she was talking to melted into nothingness before her very eyes. She got off the bus at once, and no sooner had she regained the pavement, and the conductor rung the bell, than the whole bus, instead of moving off, just faded out. Those who knew 'Bill' will aver with me that she is neither a dreamer nor the least bit imaginative, and the last person in the world to invent such a story.

Whilst we were listening to the narration of this vivid experience, we noticed the cattle were becoming uneasy, and presently a long note from a distant horn came down the wind. It echoed from ridge to ridge, from east to west of us, and after a few moments' lull, was answered from the opposite direction. The cattle by now were very restless, and we saw that they were herding themselves together in the middle of the meadow. The wind was rising and dark clouds began to race across the sky, the reeds bent their heads in passive submission, and the wind in the rigging began to moan. Then the herd began to lash their tails and raise their heads, at the same time emitting loud bellowings of fear. The next moment and we saw them all look in one direction and following it with our eyes, the cause of their distress was apparent.

A black mass of mounted men with long whips, and blowing horns, was bearing down upon them from the high ground amongst the trees beyond, and presently one of the herd, tossing his head violently and sniffing the air, called to the rest and broke into the 'double'.

With one accord they all followed, and galloping wildly about, they suddenly came straight in our direction. Things looked pretty ominous for a short while. The thundering of their hoofs across the meadow, and the wild shouting of the men rang out with a sinister hollowness on the midnight air. Then a flanking drive was made to try and head them off from the river, and their hallooings and bellowings increased as they swung across the flats.

It was a curious scene we were witnessing, for it was evident what was taking place. Some people were making a drive and stealing the cattle. But on second thought it occurred to us that those things were not done in these days of grace, and therefore what could be the explanation of such a scene? Were we back once more in the middle or even dark ages, and re-witnessing a happening of common occurrence, or what?

We were not destined, anyway, to be left very long in doubt, for the herd was heading our way in a wild, clattering stampede. Crazy-mad with excitement, they were making a final bid to avoid their pursuers, and five horsemen were coming up at the gallop to head them off once more. I can see them now. Look, there they come, stand back! My God, if those riders aren't in time! The herd is coming straight at us, making for the river. Look! Look! Never mind the cold sweat down your back; get ready, they'll be clean over the bank in a moment. Hi, get below there! They'll sweep us clean off the deck. They're coming over. Get out of the way! Look, they're here! We'll be trampled to death and sunk. . . .

With a bellow and a roar they sprang from the bank right on to the decks of all the vessels lying alongside, without a sound of hoof at all, and springing into the water, with a colossal splashing and turmoil, disappeared.

The shock was terrific, for it was one to inspire the tensest fear in the most stalwart of men. Then, looking up, we saw seven horsemen standing on the bank, their cloaks flung back, and a dull light glowing through their ribs. They were skeletons, and their eye-sockets were lighted up as well. Their grinning jaws made one feel sick. They looked straight at us and leered with a forbidding death-like defiance. The air was laden with a foetid, heavy, cattle-like odour, and a strong strain of sulphur in it.

Slowly they rode away, and after going about twenty yards, suddenly vanished.

The angry clouds ceased racing by overhead, and again the stars shone out from a clear and uninterrupted sky, the moon was up, once more we gazed across an empty meadow, and scarce a breath of air was stirring.

Beccles

Come out ye fleas, come out ye lice,
Come out ye rats, come out ye mice,
    Obey the mandate, all!
Oh, leave your nestes and walls, ye pestes,
From 'neath the floores, come out of doores,
    And answer to the call!
    (From Peter Dockett's *Ballad of Beccles, c.* 1549.)

Ugh! How I hate vermin, but when I came across this ancient verse
in a dilapidated book for children in a friend's library at Hazlebury
Bryan in Dorset a few years back, I decided there and then to wend
my enquiring feet Suffolkwards on the earliest occasion, and
accordingly made the opportunity as soon as I could and then took
advantage of it. From North to South and East to West I scoured
the country, but without much success, until one day, whilst driving
with a doctor friend of mine and his wife at Eye, I learned with
much surprise that the poem was well known to my hostess, who had
learnt it when a very little girl, and never having forgotten it, she
recited it to us over our coffee. There were nearly thirty verses, the
which I will not inflict upon you here, because I cannot remember
them, but the story which is traditional, and originally was set to a
measure, is, in effect, something between St Patrick's adventures in
Ireland and the Pied Piper of the little hamlet on the Weser. (I
could have said Hamelin straight away, but being asthmatic, I like
the name of Weser.)

Legend has it that in the days of the Black Death, which scoured
these islands in the fourteenth century, report had it that the vermin
were the cause of the pestilence (they little knew how right they were)
and that three men of the town of Beccles, where the disease was
quickly decimating the population, came forward to the town council
and stated that they had interviewed all the saints in the calendar
without any satisfaction, and as a last resource had had recourse to
the three old witches who were not allowed inside the town, and
who lived under the trees down by the dyke.

These three hags, Nancy Diver, Sally Price and Fanny Barton,

spent their dark lives in squalor and filth down on the river bank where the dyke joins the Waveney. No one ventured near their pestilential abode by day, and after nightfall nothing in the world would have coaxed any decent citizen within half-a-mile of it, for dark doings took place outside and inside their rough little shack, and their cacklings and snarlings could be heard from the centre of the town. Curls of smoke used to rise up from their fire and take curious shapes, and strange lights appeared to move about, giving rise to all manner of conjecture and misgiving. They themselves were awful to look at. Their faces were distorted, their eyes squinted, their teeth were all awry, whilst their hair was all lose and matted. They never washed and their clothes were in rags, whilst their hands resembled talons, with their long black nails like vultures' claws. Always quarrelling and screaming at each other, they were a menace to the town, but there was no one in authority strong enough to deal with them. Everyone was scared stiff of their cursings, for on one occasion, with some idea of revenge, they filled all the house-wives' puddings full of flies.

Well, the three citizens came and presented themselves before the town council and the mayor, with their proposition to free the town from the plague.

The first bowed low and said: 'My Lord Mayor and worthy Aldermen and Councillors, I am Peter Harris, a watchmaker by trade, and I can rid this town of all its trouble. How much will you give me, if I do this, because my business is very little just now?'

'One hundred marks, my good friend Harris,' replied the Mayor off his own bat, immediately.

'Methinks, alas, that's far too small,' answered Peter, 'because, as you see, to do this will cost me my life.'

'Thou hast no wife, that should be enough for one with no claims upon him by relations,' bellowed the Mayor.

'Ah me, I thought at least two thousand marks, my Lord Mayor.'

'Oh, well,' exclaimed the Mayor, leaning forward and searching him with his eyes, 'If you will promise on your oath that you will do this for your fellow-creatures, I agree, but – you will have but ten marks before you begin, and the balance when you have completed your bargain.'

'Oh, thank you, kind Mr Mayor, and this (turning to his friend) is my friend, Jonathan Bido.'

'I am Jonathan Bido, a tallow-chandler by trade, and business is very slack just now, please Mr Mayor,' said he, jumping up, 'but my friend Peter Harris cannot do this without me, and it will cost me my life, too.'

'What?' yelled the Mayor. 'What have you to do with it, anyway?'

For answer he brought forward the third man, who spoke for him:

'I am Samuel Partridge, please Mr Mayor, and I am a pedlar and stand in the market-place and sell ribbons and laces on Tuesdays and Fridays, and business isn't what it used to be, and these two friends of mine cannot do this for the town without me. How much will I receive, because this will cost me my life, too, the same as it will theirs.'

'Silence!' yelled the Mayor. 'None of ye have wives, children or relatives, and yet you want to bleed your townsfolk of six thousand marks. Not worth it.'

The three applicants bowed low and said 'Good morning!' And as they were filing out, they were suddenly recalled.

'You shall have your money,' bellowed the Mayor, but they smiled sadly and bowing low again, replied:

'Mr Mayor, and all the others, the price has gone up. It is now five thousand marks each.'

The whole Council went blue with rage, and the Mayor banged his fist down on his desk and yelled, 'No!'

Again they bowed low, and filed out. As the door closed behind them, it was suddenly opened once more, and they were called back.

'You shall have the money, ye robbers,' snapped the Mayor, fuming with rage.

'Alas, Mr Mayor and others, our price is now ten thousand marks each, and we are so sorry, but you see, it will cost us our lives and it's worth it.'

The apoplectic Mayor gasped for breath, and whilst the three candidates for martyrdom stood with respectful silence awaiting the decision, the clerk stood up, and leaning back, whispered something very private to his worship. The Chief Magistrate's face cleared, and a benign smile supplanting his purple passion, he leaned forward with great magnanimity and exclaimed:

'Make no more demands. You shall have fifteen thousand marks apiece, but only one mark on account. The balance is yours when you have done your work.'

The watchmaker, the tallow-chandler and the pedlar convened a meeting on the spot, and then agreed unanimously that they could accept the proposal. They accordingly signified their assent, a draft contract was drawn up, and they signed by impressing their thumbs on three wax seals, because they could not write their names. In return they received a whole mark each, the first instalment, bowed low, and passed out into the street. Once outside they gripped each other's hands and danced a measure in the market square.

Fifteen thousand marks each. What would they do with it? They had never dreamed of such a colossal amount. They would put it all together and make a capital pool of forty-five thousand marks, and then – but further consideration was quite beyond them for they were already mentally out of their depths, so they all repaired straight away to the three old witches, and gave them their one mark pieces. The old devils fairly snatched at the money, and then the cauldron was put on the fire.

Presently the air was filled with chatterings and screechings, the sky grew black with witches arriving from all parts on their broomsticks. They squatted around like birds of prey about a carcase, and almost pecked and snapped at each other in their clamour for priority. They perched on the branches of the trees and filled the place with their awful noise. There were thousands of them. Then the three old dames marshalled their human prey, and three black grimalkins came out of the darkness inside the shack, and perched themselves one on the shoulder of each of our three friends. The watchmaker's cat had green eyes, the tallow-chandler's purple eyes, and the pedlar's sore eyes, and they were all as mangy as mangy could be. Then old Nancy Diver called a broomstick over to her, and straddling it, she pranced around the cauldron, calling out:

Hoick-ee-hoick! Hoick! The mazzles entwoick!
Half-daffy-man-taff, the maggots galloick!

Peter Harris, Jonathan Bido and Samuel Partridge began to feel very uneasy, because just then some sparks flew out of the cauldron, and a man's dark outline formed in the steam above it. They were then given some soft wet lumps of goodness-knows-what, and were instructed to throw them into the cauldron, as they said these words:

'I, Peter Harris, Jonathan Bido, Samuel Partridge, hereby renounce all claim to the Church, its priests or its offices, and in return for the favour we ask, sell our souls unreservedly for the benefit of our fellow-creatures to His Most Gracious and Benevolent Majesty Beelzebub, King of the Red-Hot Boojums, Defender of the Unfaithful, His Serene and Most Excellent Highness the Prince of Darkness, whose glim is never dowsed, and on whose Empire not even the moon ever rises, for ever and ever, and – ever.'

The shape in the steam suddenly turned a brilliant red with fireballs for eyes, and flapping a gigantic pair of bats' wings, shook them by the hands, which nearly scorched all the skin off. He then branded them with a red-hot iron back and front so that he would know them again, and after giving them each a clout across the ear like a kick from a camel, His Satanic Majesty spat on the assembly and soared up into the sky, with all the dirty witches trailing after him like a stream of starlings. The stench that was left behind savoured of a size factory seasoned up with a dash of concentrated cacodyl and assafortida.

'Go now to your houses and fetch out your instruments and come back at once,' croaked old Fanny Barton, and the three initiates repaired to their dwellings and returned as quickly as they could.

These old black-artists breathed on their instruments, and then spat in their faces, telling them to prance through the streets playing their music, and that all the vermin would flock out of the houses and follow them. They would then lead their procession down to the dyke, and there they would all go to ground in a hole beneath the cauldron.

And Peter, Jonathan and Sam did as they were bid. They pranced up and down every street making a fearful row, and all the rats and mice came out and followed them, also all the other nasties as well, until the streets were full of vermin. Those which couldn't keep up rode on the backs of those who could, and after several hours the long procession – there were two miles and a half of it – reached the weird sisters' abode, and as the three musicians kept plugging away at their music so the rodents with their parasitic burdens passed into the fire and vanished into the earth. The following day the plague had abated, and in two days it was gone altogether. The town was free.

Peter Harris, Jonathan Bido and Samuel Partridge were sent for by the Town Clerk, their money was procured and counted out ready for them, but – they never turned up to claim it, and, I fear me, never will. The money was sunk in a fund to provide little nigger-girls in foreign parts with little lace frillies, and little nigger-boys with pocket handkerchiefs to keep the sun off, by the Anti-Freckle League.

What happened to our three heroes, did you say? Well, as soon as they had cleared the town, in fulfilment of their bonds, all the meat fell off their bones, they sizzled inside, and were consumed by spontaneous internal combustion.

And so it comes about that every year on the night of 31 August, if you moor up close to the bank near the dyke, but not in it, and wait patiently, you may see three shrivelled skeletons dressed in short breeches, loose coats and old shapeless soft hats, come prancing along from the direction of the town, each playing respectively his lute, shawm and glockenspiel. Always in single file they keep this up, traversing every street in Beccles, and followed back to the dyke by a never-ending black seething mass, crawling all over itself on the ground and ending in the dying embers of a fire, which you have to prepare beforehand on the spot where originally stood the old witches cauldron.

Sometimes you can hear the concourse of witches arrive, and the air becomes stuffy and dark, and the noise intense, and I have heard it said that Old Nick himself has been seen in that neighbourhood very often, when he has been able to get away from his other duties.

Sir Malcolm Stoddart, in a letter to his great friend, the Hon. Sidney Walters, dated 3 of September 1897, states:

'This is the second time I have seen this wonderful phenomenon, but Dick, who accompanied me this last occasion has seen it no less than seven times.'

Calder, to his great friend Sheldon (*c.* 1642) in the Heiner Manuscripts at the Bodlein says:

'Methinks the people of Beccles should be well-pleased in that eache yeare on 31 August theyre three championes and martyres much cleansey the towne by ridding it of all creepynge thynges, castynge them into ye fire on ye bank-side.'

I haven't seen this yet, but am off there this next summer, come what will or come what may. I want to meet those three skeletal musicians and hear their chthonic strains. I would also like their autographs while I am about it.

Stokesby

Have you never heard of Willum of Stokesby, sometimes known as the 'Gimpie'? Ah, well, he is an amusing fellow, a sort of modern Puck, and yet his best friend would be quite unable to find anything Shakespearean, dreamy, or ethereal about him. The people of Stokesby aren't too keen on him, as you may well imagine, although he is only seen there between Easter and Mid-September.

It was George Horsburgh who first told me about him, and he met him on the jetty there. The old man wanted to take his head-line and make fast for him, but George nipped ashore, put it around a bollard himself, dropped a shilling in Willum's hand, and it fell through to the ground. When George had retrieved it he looked up and Willum had vanished. George, to steady his nerves, adjourned for a 'quick one', and got into conversation with a funny looking antique, replete in 'Whitechapel' and corduroys, who laughed, or rather cackled, when he told him about it.

'That must 'ave bin ole Willum again,' remarked the old man, and tossing off his beer, wiped his mouth on a huge red handkerchief and simply faded away where he stood, leaving George more nonplussed then ever.

The amusing part about Willum is that you never can be sure if you are talking to him or not, because of his extraordinary faculty of simulation.

I once heard a man go to another on the quay there and say: 'Excuse me, are you Willum?'

It happened not to be the person in question, and offence was sadly taken of it. The injured party snapped out, 'No, I'm not,' and swinging round on his heel, walked away.

You cannot be too careful, because Willum has apparently annoyed this delectable little riverside spot for many centuries. No one seems to know him or anything concerning him. He is such a genial person, too, full of desire to help others and do little odd jobs when he can for them. He has no home in the village and no one can tell you anything about him, except that he just comes and goes, and is quite harmless. Little children tease him sometimes, and once a small girl caught hold of his coat and pulled at him. To her intense surprise he melted into nothingness before her eyes, and left her little hand quite empty.

One day the village policeman – not the present one – thought Willum was a bit out of control and locked him up for being 'the worse for'. Everybody laughed at him for being such a 'loon', which made the minion of the law very annoyed, but his surprise can be imagined when on unlocking the door he found there was no Willum at all. The next day Willum was down on the quay hanging around as was his usual wont, but the 'bobby' refused even to look at him or have anything to say to him. It was months before the villagers let him forget this episode.

A doctor friend of mine, who hired a little craft called the *Harlequin*, came alongside one day last year and gave Willum two shillings to get some beer. Willum brought the liquor and gave him eightpence change in coppers. As he 'dropped' him sixpence for himself, Willum touched his hat, said 'Thank 'ee, 'bor!' and melted into absolute nothingness on the spot. You might like to hear my friend describe it. These things have the virtue of happening in broad daylight.

A 'shell-back' parson was telling me about him one day when I happened to mention that I knew several people who had met him. This was his version of what occurred to him.

'My little ship, the *White Phantom*, was coming up stream against the tide, when I thought it would be a good idea to fill our fresh-water tanks, so I made to come alongside. An elderly looking old bean came forward to take our head-line, and dropped it over a bollard on the quay. I went below, shut off the engine, turned off the petrol, and told my two little boys to put the fenders over the side. Imagine my surprise when they started calling to me excitedly. I raced up on deck and took in the situation at a glance. When I saw him, as I thought, drop the head-line over the bollard there was no bollard there, and we went drifting down with the current.

I really was angry and felt I could have knocked the old fellow's head off for what was nothing short of a dirty trick. We could have piled up and strained our timbers badly waiting for the tide to return. It was no good looking and cursing; action was imperative, so we 'chucked over' there and then, right in the fairway. I didn't care. If we were in the way of other vessels they could jolly well go round us, that was all. Now, to re-start the engine. It was a good engine in its way, but – a devil to start. Ha – don't be shocked at anything I say. I'm trying to get used to it myself, but it's very difficult. Well, I went below and took off my coat, waistcoat, collar and stock, put on a right-hand glove, took several deep breaths, and then seizing the

handle, gave her a half-turn – and she started. Such a thing had never been heard of in all her long – well, not very long – history. Then I raced up on deck to the little deck-house to adjust the controls, when she conked out. What new cruel fate was this upon me?

'I returned to the engine-room, tried to flood the carburetter – h'mph, no petrol. Now what were we going to do? We had plenty when we began the day's run. Perhaps the petrol-pipe was stuffed up, so I took a spanner and put it on the union beneath the auto-vac, when my eyes dilated widely. I had omitted to turn the fuel on again. This omission was soon rectified, the carburetter flooded, and the first pull over she back-fired like a camel lashing out. I was flung clean across the engine-room, and with the starting-lever still tightly clutched in my right hand I succeeded in smashing a side-window, and cutting my arm rather miserably. At the same moment "Demoniac" – my engine's name – emitted a piercing report, which shook the entire neighbourhood, and a shoot of the blackest of soot, over four hundred yards long, spread itself on the surface of the water and polluted the entire river.

'Then in my rage – parson or no parson, I was fuming – I leapt at the engine and struck it, deliberately and with malice afore-thought struck it a violent blow with the starting-handle. I had to strike somebody, so I let my pent-up malevolence vent itself upon the cause of the trouble, when, to my intense surprise, "Demoniac", without any pulling over or winding up, started of her own accord. You can say I was tight, or asleep, or any darned thing you like, but that doesn't explain any of it. I fled above to the controls and brought the ship up against the current, whilst the boys winched up the hook, and slowly we crept back up-stream until we berthed once more along-side the little quay, and I sprang ashore this time with the head-line myself and made fast to a large ring-bolt.

'My next move was to stop the engine and then look around for that stupid fellow who had let us down. There was not a soul in sight who tallied with him, so I spoke to another old man about him, who listened attentively and was very sympathetic and offered to come aboard and make the window good.

'"Let's 'ave a look at it, 'bor," he said. So we walked over to the vessel together, and then I had another surprise. The broken window was gone, not a trace of it was left. It had been replaced in that short space of time without anybody being the slightest bit aware of the reparation. Then I told him about the behaviour of 'Demoniac', and he laughed. This annoyed me a little and I said:

'"It's nothing to laugh at. The silly old idiot might have caused no end of trouble, even to loss of the ship."

141

'"I'm sorry," he replied. "You're quite right."

'"Well, don't you agree with me it was a darned stupid thing to do. Playing the silly ass like that, you never know what might happen."

'"Yes," replied the old man, "but he never meant no harm, of that I'm sure."

'"Perhaps not," I answered, "but the damage would have been the same whether he meant it or not."

'"Oh, but he did make the damage good, as you must admit."

'"Yess," I answered, a trifle irritated at the old boy's attitude, "but tell me, why do you hold a brief, or appear to, for this damfool old clown, who is not only a loon and a half-wit, but a very unsafe person. Is this Willum a particular friend of yours?"

'"I *am* Willum," blurted out the old man, and before I could recover from my surprise, he had melted into space before my very eyes.'

All of which, as I am trying to point out, goes to prove that one has to be very careful at Stokesby to whom one speaks. The people of this village are not the tiniest bit uneasy about Willum, but some of them will actually tell you they know nothing about him, which is very disconcerting, for you can never be sure that you are not talking to him himself. To those of the village who do not mind talking about our mysterious friend, these unexpected happenings to visitors are a source of great joy, and serve as a mental recreation and something to talk about until the next season opens.

Capt. Bellamy Bliss, G.C.B., the Commodore to the North Sea Yacht Squadron, in September, 1911, wrote an interesting description of him in the *Navigators' Gazette*, Vol. 37, pages 321–2, which is worth quoting:

'At the small and old-world village of Stokesby on the Bure, we came alongside and made fast to the little quay, where at the moment there were many people, who had collected from every quarter to see us arrive. The *Iaia* is a fine vessel for her size, being eighty-four feet long with a beam of twenty-one, and very shallow draught. She carries a crew of five and her deck is a joy to behold for cleanliness and polish. Snow-white all over with brass and gun-metal fittings, she is a positive dream-ship and compels attention. I was sitting on the after-hatch when we arrived, and an old country woman came aboard to see if we required any fresh fruit, eggs, butter, or poultry. I referred her to the purser and she went below. Presently the purser came to me from the fo'c'stle and enquired if he might go ashore for stores as we needed fresh vegetables, fruit and milk. I told him that an old woman had just gone below to see him, so he went after her. In a few moments he returned saying that there was no "old lady" aboard. But she had actually spoken to me, and I had sent her down to him, so I went below myself to find her. I searched every cabin, saloon, corridor and store-room, but the purser was right. On coming on deck once more, there was the old biddy talking to the purser from the jetty.

'"How did you come up from below?" I enquired of her.

'"I didn't come up," she replied with a strange leer.

'"Oh, I see," I replied.

'"No, you don't see. You're blind," she answered, with a bland smile.

'"Oh, and how long have I been blind, pray?" I asked, light suddenly beginning to dawn on me.

'"Always," she retorted, putting down her basket, "or you'd have seen I didn't go down. What you thought you saw and what actually did happen are two different things, and don't argyfy with me, young man."

'There was no reply to this sort of person. The purser looked at me very puzzled as I walked away, and an hour later came to me with a parcel which he said the "old lady" had brought with the dairy produce he had ordered. On removing its wrapper there was a fine large capon all ready trussed and dressed for roasting, and it was addressed "To the Blind Captain from William." I could not make out who William could be, so I enquired of an elderly native who was leaning on a thick stick when I stepped ashore. I noticed him because he touched his hat to me, which courtesy I returned and spoke to him.

'"Do you happen to know the old lady who sells fowls and butter and eggs to visitors, and who came aboard the *Iaia* this afternoon."

'"Oh, aye, 'bor," he replied with a kindly smile. "Ah know 'er well."

'"Come and show me where to get a drink," I said, wondering if he would accept.

'"That's very kind of 'ee, 'bor. Let's go on to there," and he indicated a very pleasing looking caravanserai with his stick. In the bar he had a pint of barley-wine, and I a half. (Talk about good stuff, you have to go to the country places for it. I never have tasted such wonderful beer in my life). Anxious to learn what I could of the "old lady", I asked a very pointed question:

'"Tell me," I said, "who is the dear old dame who came aboard today?"

'"Ah-ha," he replied, chuckling to himself, "she were a dear, were she?"

'"I should just say she was. Do you know she brought me a parcel containing a splendid fowl. From William."

'"Oh – ah, 'bor. She don't mean no 'arm. She likes doin' little things like that, 'specially for strangers."

'"Yes, I can understand that," I replied, "but who is she?"

'"She *is* Willum," he answered.

'"Ah-ha," I exclaimed, trying to see a joke somewhere. "Yes, I see, but who *is* William?"

'He looked at me out of the tail of his eye and winked, and draining his mug, placed it on the counter, and after a rough wipe of his mouth, replied:

'"I am."

'I realised now that he was having a joke with me, so I drained my tot and looked around, but he had – gone. Not left by the door or the window, but simply evaporated before my eyes into emaciated nothingness.'

This year I hope to stop at Stokesby, if only for two things. One to fill a beaker with barley-wine, and the second for the off-chance of meeting Willum; but if you, dear reader, should happen to be there, too, and take it into your head to enquire if I am Willum, I shall most certainly say 'Yes', and lead you gently by the arm to the local vineyard, where, I warn you now, it will cost you quite a lot of money.

Hickling

Sweet are thy flowers in June, in June, in June,
Fragrant and fresh are thy gentle blooms.
They come in the Spring,
They list the zephyrs sing,
How wonderful the flowers in June,
How lovely they are.

The voice was that of a woman's, beautiful, soft, caressing in its cadences, rising and falling like the gentle evening breeze on a quiet summer's evening. Somehow the refrain seemed familiar, somewhere those strains seemed to echo back into the hidden realms of memory, the gentle melody carrying one away in a kind of ecstacy, which was a nepenthe for mind and body after a hard day's sailing. As we lay spread out on the deck of the *Whitelady*, the dulcet voice floated gently across the Broad, the birds ceased their evensong to listen, and the evening star idled on his way across the dimming sky to lend an ear to what he might not hear again for many moons. The reed-warblers hung on to their rushes forgetful of their own music, and everything around became so still and quiet, that it seemed as though all Nature had stopped to listen. When the soul is stirred with sweet emotion one forgets one's environment, and is borne away, mentally transported as it were, on a magic carpet of intense ecstasy. And this is exactly what did happen, for we were all enchanted, and when the singer ceased her beautiful song, we gazed at each other in mute approval.

It was the mate who broke the spell, and being a young man who has ideas of his own concerning women, he suddenly blurted out, 'Lovely, lovely, the boys are here. Lovely, lovely!' We all enjoyed his subtle allusion, and were very glad we were here, but it was a case of 'cherchez la femme'. To hear a gorgeous voice with the flexibility of that of the nightingale, clear, resonant, and delightfully pitched, and not to see the singer, lent an added mystery to the occasion and set one tingling with excitement and curiosity to discover the owner and her whereabouts.

The following day I spoke to a parson about it. He was fishing in a boat close by, having undoubtedly a rest from his human piscatorial endeavours and indulging in the more certain type of angling, whereby one can play a fish, finally haul it in, and place it in the creel with the certain knowledge that there it will remain.

'Ho-ho,' he remarked, taking a good look at me, 'so you've heard it, too. Well, well, now isn't that interesting?'

'She seems to be known to you,' I replied, mentally preparing a scheme wherewith to sound him, and so obtain some information.

He was a jolly sort of person, with a ready twinkle in his eye, and by his tone of voice hailed from Oxford, and, I thought by the sound of his i's he had 'flourished at Eton.' His demeanour was most unwittingly attractive, and his general presence suggested an ancestry of quality.

'Known to me?' he said, his eyes dancing with sheer joy, 'I should just think she is. I come here every year for a fortnight, and always at this time, in order to hear her, and do a spot of fishing as an excuse for my coming.'

'Have you ever seen her?' I enquired coaxingly. 'I expect she must be very beautiful.'

'My dear sir, she is so beautiful that her voice, lovely as it is, falls sadly short of what it should be, or what you would expect if you but once set eyes on her.'

'She must indeed be more than beautiful.'

'My boy,' he was now becoming confidential, 'only those who are supremely psychic have ever gazed upon her beauty.'

'Then,' I replied, 'from that, I can take it no one has ever yet had that good fortune.'

'H'm – p'raps, perhaps not,' he answered, seeming on his guard.

'Tell me something about her,' I said, feeling he was desirous of keeping a good deal to himself. 'Is she ancient, medieval or modern?'

'Well, I'll tell you. She's quite a modern. I might almost say recent. You see, it's this way. She is looking for her man, and as he always loved Hickling Broad, she comes here and sings for him every night in June. I have heard it said that only those who knew her can ever hear her singing. Did you, my friend, ever hear of her when she was on this earth and had a body like yours or mine, for apparently she must have been well known?'

'Well, now, how should I know? What was her name? Do you know it?'

'Yes,' he replied.

'How do you know it, then?' I enquired eagerly.

'You must not ask me that. I am not permitted to tell you or anyone. She has been coming here for the last three years, and always in June. She sings, sings, and sings her little heart away all night long in the hope that her man will hear her and come to her once more. He is what they call "out in the grey".'

I interrupted him. 'You're a spiritualist?' I exclaimed.

'Well, is not God a Spirit? Is not everything that is abstract spiritual? Even a single thought, is not that non-material, subjective, ethereal or spiritual? A thought has no physical existence, then indeed must it not be spiritual, in so far that it has a definite existence, but no physical body or condition? The same as yourself, which you have never seen nor ever will see, but only the physical mechanism through which you manifest yourself. All men have two beings: a physical and a spiritual. This beautiful creature has discarded her physical mechanism and still continues in her spiritual body. All of which you undoubtedly consider to be absolute tosh, and me, mad.'

'On the contrary,' I answered, full of intense interest. 'I quite agree with you and have always accepted and believed what you have just advanced.'

'You mean that? Then you are a spiritualist, too. Spiritualism is not a creed, a religion or a denomination, it is merely a belief in metaphysical truth and revelation. Have you ever been to a séance? A real one; not the make-believe stuff and nonsense of the professional medium, but a home circle?'

I admitted that I had not, but would welcome the opportunity.

'Very well, my friend, may I ask you to join ours tonight?'

I said I would, and so it was arranged that we would hold the 'sitting' on the deck of my little ship that evening about six bells in the centre of the Broad, that he would bring three friends, and I should make, with 'Bill', my winch-hand, a fifth and sixth. 'Bill' is very psychic, though she is only a slip of a young girl, and not yet seventeen.

That night, 'Bert', our cabin-boy – another feminine sapling of about 'Bill's' age – and the mate took the dinghy and went off for a night's fishing, whilst 'Bill' and I prepared the deck with cushions, arranging them in a circle, and a wander-light, with red cellulose enamel on the bulb, and a long lead plugged into a deck-fitting.

At five minutes to eleven we heard the gentle plash of our visitors' sculls, and in a few minutes their dinghy came alongside.

It was a perfect night, and scarce a breath of air was stirring, and although the sky was clear and the stars were very bright, there was no moon. The conditions were ideal, and we sat ourselves down in a circle with the lamp in the centre ready to be switched on when required.

I omitted to mention that we had the gramophone on deck, and a favourite record of mine, 'Oh, for the wings of a dove.' in readiness to begin.

We sat quite still for a long while just holding hands and completing the circuit. Our parson friend said the 'Pater Noster', and after that we started this beautiful anthem. The boy's voice that was singing rang out loud and clear, and according to 'Bert', it was quite distinct at the far end of the Broad.

As the final cadences rose and fell we heard another voice, richer by far, and infinitely more distinct than the solo-chorister's, joining in. It was most weird and uncanny, and yet somehow we were none of us afraid.

At last the record was finished, and to our intense gratification the girl singer continued alone. She sang and sang, oh, how she sang! But I had heard that voice before, and in a soft whisper I told the clergyman, who was next to me.

'Yes,' he answered very softly. 'Last night.' But I was certain I had heard that voice long before then.

Presently the singing ceased, and we waited in absolute quietude. The parson was certain something would happen, if we could be patient enough, but I had my doubts. Anyway, I was not to be kept very long in a state of uncertainty, for the words were scarcely out of his mouth than everyone in the circle shuddered. It was not a quiver of fear, but of intense cold blowing on our faces and like cold water running down the spine. The sort of feeling when all the warmth suddenly seems to leave your body, and the skin feels what is commonly called 'goosey' all over. Then one of the parson's friends gave a catch in his breath, his head dropped forward on to breast, and in a second he was fast asleep.

'He's off,' remarked our cleric friend. 'He always goes off like that.'

'Entranced?' I asked under my breath.

'Yes,' he replied.

As I have already said the night was warm and mild, just as a June night should be, but we were almost shivering with cold internally, although externally we were quite warm. In other words we were all 'giving-out', and the conditions were 'building-up'. This is one of those phases which invariably precede something very important.

If a slight digression may be permitted for the benefit of those who know nothing of these things, I would like to mention in a few words what actually happens at a séance. Every sitter produces and projects a certain quantity of telekinetic energy and so contributes with the others present to the amount necessary for 'building-up' what are called 'conditions', to provide the 'controlling' spirit who is going to operate through the medium with a vehicle for his manifestation.

According to the amount of telekinetic energy available, so are the conditions sufficient or otherwise. At the termination of the sitting this is restored to the donors, so that no one may feel the loss of it afterwards. The more psychic a sitter happens to be, the more sensitive he is, which amounts to saying that he has the more tele-kinetic energy, which in turn allows him to put-out or give-out more than is usual, and so becomes the more a valuable and helpful factor in the production of phenomena, and an easy channel through which the 'other side' can operate or 'come through'. A medium, therefore, is one who can give out enormous quantities of this energy, and so becomes an instrument through which the 'other side' can communicate.

Well, to continue. Here we were out on deck, sous les belles étoilles, everything around was still, and the 'conditions' perfect. Presently, the medium, the entranced one, gave a slight start, then a shiver shook his frame from head to toe, and we saw a faintly illuminated vapour forming in the centre of the circle. It rose up from the deck, and slowly began to shape itself. From the upper part the features of somebody began to develop, just like they would on a photographic plate, with this difference that the picture was not a negative but a positive. Then the body began gently to form itself, swathed in a flowing garment of filmy, clinging vapour. Gradually this extra-ordinary apparition commenced to become steroscopic in its relief, and finally, when its development was complete, there stood before us a most beautiful girl, whom I recognised immediately. She was the 'Russian Nightingale', the girl whose voice had charmed the late Emperor Nicholas and the entire court of the Romanoffs, and who during the bloody massacres of the Revolution had managed to escape from her native country, which very few other princesses had been able to do. She was a lady of exalted birth, and in addition to being a princess in her own right, she had married an English baron, the scion of a famous English family whose estates were all in Russia. They had separated in order to facilitate their flight from their hell-ridden country. She had disguised herself as a boy and gone to work as a labourer, travelling by night and sleeping under hedges and ditches until she gained the frontier. Her husband had joined Denikin's army, and there lost a leg. He was put upon a ship at Odessa and spirited away out of it whilst the going was good.

They met eventually in Vienna, and there, after a rest, she turned bread-winner, because the baron's lungs had given out and he was hopelessly incapacitated. This heroic little soul just worshipped her man, and worked as hard as she could by singing in order to keep a roof over their heads. From Vienna they came to Paris, where she had originally been trained, and from there to England. It was in London that they both eventually came under my medical care, and by dint of personal introductions, they just managed to keep going. She, poor frail little flaxen-curled child, was very delicate. Although she was twenty-five she looked for all the world like a little girl of ten, tiny and petite, with a shock of natural flaxen curls, which wobbled when she shook her pretty head, and were kept just tied together at the back in a way that made them more prominent at the sides. Her large, round, pleading eyes went straight to your heart and everybody loved, simply loved little Princess Vera. When she sang, she could only keep it up for a fortnight, because it so exhausted her, for she sang, not with her voice alone, but with her entire body, and if that wasn't very much, it was all she had, and although she was able to earn good money as singers go, at her rate of going she had to earn enough in six months to support herself and her husband for a year.

It was a terrible strain for her, but she stuck it, and worked on determinedly. At the London Coliseum I have seen the place fairly rock with excitement after her first song. It was the same wherever she went, but her audiences little realised she was feeding their pleasures with her very life-blood itself. To her and her husband the door of my house was ever open, and a ready welcome always awaited them, and somehow the whole atmosphere seemed to change the moment she entered, the same as it does in the presence of a really holy person. The air appears to become charged with their own personality.

Hers was indeed a very sad life for one so young and lovely, and at last she managed to procure a contract for what is known theatrically as the 'South African Tour', and away she went, the baron with her. South Africa went mad over her, and from there she went to the 'States'. That was the last I had heard of them till the news of her death reached me indirectly two years ago.

And here she was now reincarnated and standing before me.

To the uninitiated this would have come as a terrific shock. To me it was a most unexpected and agreeable happening. To say I was surprised is to put it mildly, for the princess was the last person in the world I would have expected on such an occasion. The story of her passing had never to my knowledge been confirmed, and here was the confirmation before me.

Another slight digression here if you will allow me, for I consider it right that the reader should know that, although we had all supped, none of us had touched a drop of liquor all that day, and therefore any artificial stimulus to our powers of imagination had been rigidly excluded. We were all, excepting the medium, absolutely as wide awake and conscious as we are now. The simple truth needs no assistance to make it the more impressive.

On seeing me, her blue magnetic eyes opened wider than ever I had known them, and apparently she was as surprised as I was, and coming straight across, she held out her hands.

'Captain!' she exclaimed. 'Oh, my dear, very dear friend. What joy is this?'

'Vera,' I replied, 'are you really the same who used to come and let me help you?'

'Oh, yes, my dear one. I have not changed, have I?' Her voice had still the same timbre, and rose and fell with the same delicious inflections that endeared her to everyone the moment she spoke.

'Not one little bit,' I answered, filled with a kind of holy joy at the prospect of perhaps being able to be of service to her once more. 'Tell me,' I went on, 'why are you here?'

'Ah, my dear Captain, my joy at meeting you again is beyond everything. I am looking for "Man".' (She always called him 'Man', because she admired him so). 'Have you seen him?'

'Alas, no, princess——' She interrupted me.

'Not princess, now, Captain. Just your little friend, Vera. There are no princesses here. I wish I could find "Man". I sing, sing, sing, in the hope that he will hear my voice and come to me, but he does not come. Oh, where is "Man", my dear "Man"?'

'Tell me, Vera, dear,' I said, 'why do you come to Hickling Broad for him. Do you expect to find him here?'

'Yes, Captain dear. When we were in England, he and I came up here for a rest, and he loved me dearly and said to me: "Remember, my little Poupée – you remember, he always called me that – if ever we are parted again, we will come back and meet here, on this broad water so like the lake at our home in Alexandrovak, and we will come out upon it together, and you shall sing to me, and awaken once again the memories of my lost home, my father and my mother, and – You!"'

'Let me help you,' I replied, realising her sorrow. 'When did you pass over?'

'Three years since, or is it a hundred? I don't know. I have been asleep such a long time. They found "Man", you know, in a forest somewhere near New York. He was dying, and they brought him in to the big town, and there he passed. He could not bear my working for him any longer and he went away by himself to die, so that in his great love for his little Poupée, he should not be a drag on her any longer. When I heard the news I was standing on a balcony outside my window a hundred and fifty feet above the street level. When they picked me up, I was sleeping, but when I awakened I was back here where we had pledged ourselves to meet. And I still am waiting, waiting, waiting. Do you think he will come?'

'Keep on singing, Vera dear, and he is bound to hear you soon. Will you come and see me in London, sometimes, because I cannot often get the time to come here?'

'Dear, dearest of friends, of course I will come to you. And you will help me to find "Man"? Whenever you call me, remember I will be with you.' And stepping forward, she planted a tender, warm kiss upon my forehead.

Slowly she faded away, back into the realm of space and invisibility, but we could all hear her dulcet voice getting further and further away, until it faded out into the silence of the night.

The medium gave a little shudder, opened his eyes feebly, and in a moment completely recovered his former self.

The parson looked at me with wide open eyes and exclaimed: 'Well, who'd have believed it? I've come here for the last three years and never seen her before as I have tonight. She has only been faintly visible, but sufficiently for me to make out her beauty, but I have always heard her singing. Is it not wonderful, my friend? And fancy her coming to us tonight completely materialised? And having known you! That beats me. It is beyond all belief. Let's go below and have some hot coffee.'

Stalham

One summer's evening – to be exact it was 3 June last year – we had sailed over in the tender *Stormpot* from Barton Broad to do a spot of shopping in the attractive little village of Stalham. We lingered long and inquisitively in the old church, and admired the ancient font with the famous apostles carved on its side. Tradition has it that these 'gentlemen', at every new quarter of the moon, come down from their cold stone nitches and gambol like schoolboys and chase each other around the nave. So be it, but I, for one, am less credulous than the bewhiskered old chap who told me this with all the seriousness of advancing years, and indicated each 'gent' in turn with his rubber-ferruled stick.

I rather liked him though, for after all, if he believed it, he would naturally desire his listeners to do likewise.

'There an't much yer, 'bor,' he said, wiping his nose with a dexterous curve of his wrist. 'You want to go to Ingham. Yes, it's Ingham you want. Only a mile away, and scarce that. I'd go over there if I was you. You goes goosey all over the very moment you enters the church.'

This was the sort of information that appealed to me, so we slipped him a token and departed for Ingham.

If you have never been there, it is your bounden duty to go, and I can assure you it will charm you beyond all forgetfulness. The dear old 'Whitechapel' at Stalham was right, and we no sooner set foot inside its sacred portal than a cold, chilly shiver vibrated down my back from head to toe. The same delightful feeling when the barber wiggles the cold steel clippers around the back of your neck. I like that sensation personally and always feel a little regret when he replaces them on the shelf over the basin.

The church is the only thing of interest in the village, stands on high ground, and is a very well-proportioned edifice. The moiety of the manor of Ingham dates back to the days of Coeur de Lion, when it was vested in John de Ingham. One of his descendants, Oliver de Ingham, was a great friend of Edward the Second, who made him the governor of several castles, Sénechal of Gascoigne, and Warden of

Guyenne, in France, as a reward for his loyalty and valorous prowess at arms in defence of his King. The church, which is dedicated to the Holy Trinity, was built on the site of a much more ancient one in 1360, and was appropriated by Thomas Percy, Bishop of Norwich. Sir Oliver founded a priory there for the use of 'one prior, a sacrist, and six monks of the Order of Trinity and St Victor'. The remains of these are still to be seen in the churchyard. Under an arch in the north side of the chancel lies the sculptured effigy of Sir Oliver, and on the side of his tomb is inscribed, 'Mounsier Oliver de Ingham gist icy, et Dame Elizabeth sa compagne, que tuy Dieu de les almes, dit mercy.'

Over by the rood-loft is an altar-tomb with sculptured figures of Sir Roger de Bois and his wife Margaret. The knight is in complete armour, his head rests upon the body of a Saracen, and at his feet lies a hound with its paws resting upon a gauntlet. His arms argent, two bars with a canton gules; over all a fillet (sable) may still be seen on his surtout, whilst his lady's robe shows her arms quartered with those of her husband. In the year 1800 the brasses, which were among the finest in the country, were stolen from the church.

'Ah, 'bor,' exclaimed the old custos who had procured the keys and was showing us around, 'there be foine tales told of these two knights. They may be stone, but they do say every year they leaves their missuses and go for a walk down by the Broad. At night, too. Old Mrs Trayner, who used to live in the big house over yonder – housekeeper or somethin', I think she were – was comin' 'ome one night after bein' out to a friend's party, when she walked right into 'em, the two of 'em, down by the Staithe. Someone 'eard 'er scream, and when they got to 'er she had had a stroke with the fright of it, and were ill for a long time. When do they walk, did you ask, 'bor? Why, now let me see. Oh, my memory's awful sometimes. Oh, ah, I got it. Second of August. That's it. Second of August, it be. I remember, 'cause my Aunt Lizzie what's now ninety-three has her birthday the day after, and she were born on the third of August, a month too soon, 'er mother bein' frightened the night before by them two fellers what ought to know better, I says.'

'But tell me, friend, how do you know it's these two gentlemen who go night-walking?'

'Easy, that is. These tombs 'ave been watched 'eaps o' times, and they actually 'ave been seen to get up and step off their moniments, leaving their ladies still as they were and an empty place beside each of 'em. They've been followed down to the water and back, and up on to their places again beside their wives.'

As it was now 21 May, it meant that if I wanted to be an eye-witness of this extraordinary phenomenon, I must return on August the 1st. This was a difficulty, in fact, almost an impossibility, but as I am not one to be baulked by an obstacle like this, I came away thinking very hard, and that night after supper put on my pipe and worked out a plan of campaign.

On my return to town I took the opportunity of having a chat with my director, and knowing him to be a man intensely interested in psychic phenomena, it did not take him long to become excitedly enthusiastic about it, and exclaimed:

'You must have another week, dear boy, and you and I will go down together. Leave it to me and it can easily be arranged.' So it was left to him, and in due course we found ourselves with three others and a small motor cruiser down at Stalham.

The three others were General Sir David Ogilvie, K.C.B., G.C.S.I., F.S.A., and a well-known writer to the *Cornhill* on psychic science; Dr Robinson Wheeler, Regious Professor of Natural Science at Cambridge; and George Oxenholme, D.Sc., F.R.S., and Hallurian Reader on Psychology at the University at Durham. Matthew Gordon, my director friend, who was running the adventure, was an Antiquary, and a fellow member of the Royal Institution of Great Britain.

On arrival at the Staithe, we tied up and sorted out our impedimenta, especially the cinema camera which Gordon takes everywhere with him. I tried to reason with him that it would be impossible to shoot the scene on account of insufficient light, but he replied that these psychic conditions produce a light of their own inappreciable to the human eye, yet quite enough to react upon the sensitive emulsion of a film. We made our purpose known to the vicar, who was a real sportsman and did everything he could to help us. A second camera was introduced with a flash apparatus, in order to snap the tombs when deserted by their domiciliary occupants.

I am quite aware that to speak in this strain must sound perfectly ridiculous to the materialist whose empiricism will not allow him to imagine that a body once dead can ever behave again in the manner to which it was accustomed prior to its decease, but that cannot be helped. Let us listen first and criticise after.

It was the 1st August, and Matthew Gordon examined very closely the tombs and the light, also the best positions for fixing the stand-camera, and took three pictures of each of the tombs straight away. Whilst he was taking the last plate, something pushed the camera clean over, and this in broad daylight, about three in the afternoon. It was a time exposure with a ·32 F diaphragm, and no one was near the tripod when it happened. It was not that the feet slipped, because the spikes at each foot were well-set, and the blow that knocked the camera over was just as though it had been swept aside by someone in passing. Not a sound was heard except the crash of the machine, but it was soon restored to its position and the shutter closed. No window was open at the time and no ordinary draught could have carried it over, for it was a heavy apparatus, not a flimsy quivering one that would vibrate almost without provocation. All this may appear of no importance, and were it not for what came of it, I would not have troubled to mention the incident.

On the following afternoon everything was fixed and made ready for the evening, the flash lamp prepared, and every precaution taken that nothing should be disturbed. Powdered starch was sprinkled all around the bases of both tombs for a distance of six feet. A very fine wire was laid across both double effigies, and connected with an electrical contrivance that would, on being disturbed, complete an electrical circuit and start a dictaphone with a loud receiver. I took the notes of the entire proceeding, whilst Gordon operated his cinema camera. Dr Wheeler attended to the flash apparatus, and Oxenholme was detailed to look after the recording apparatus. The General took charge of the door of the church and held the key.

I have had many long waits in my time, but from half-past ten p.m. till a quarter-past midnight seemed interminable, almost an eternity. We kept deadly still and tried not to make the slightest sound, and if ever an atmosphere could be called eerie, then that in

this church became almost intolerably so. Outside, the clouds were scudding across a light but moonless sky, and the ticking of a clock somewhere only served to add to the weird chilliness of this ancient church. The smell which is always present in old buildings, that subtle aroma of damp vaults and stale bones, seemed to be intensified as the hours wore on, but we stuck to our posts unflinchingly, and presently we heard and felt distinctly an icy cold breeze waft itself through the nave. We knew, then, that something was about to happen.

We had not long to wait. There was quite sufficient light for us, now that our retinae had become accustomed to it, to see everything in the church, and, just as the light from without streamed in through the windows, we heard an ominous crack, as of stone being broken; cold Niagaras coursed down our spines, and we were rewarded by seeing the effigy of Sir Oliver de Ingham definitely move, and then sit up. His stone body was now taking life, and his carved armour had changed to burnished steel. A low whistle then awakened the faithful hound at his feet, and picking up his steel gauntlet, Sir Oliver threw his legs over the side of his tomb and stood erect beside his resting place. As he stood there he was the personification of everything knightly and noble. He was a fine, upstanding, stalwart man with a sad but determined face, and I shall never forget the impressive picture he made as he stood there, holding his steel helm under his left arm, and looking eagerly around. The dictaphone had started recording, and the clanking of his armour rang through the length and breadth of this sacred fane. Whatever feelings we might have experienced were lost in our awe and interest in what we were witnessing.

Almost at the same moment another crack was heard, and then we saw Sir Oliver clank across to the tomb of Sir Roger de Bois, and touching the stone effigy of this gallant knight with his mailed hand, the recumbent statue of Sir Roger sat up, rubbed his eyes, and looked around. Then his carved granitic armour suddenly changed to polished metal, and he descended from his place by the side of his wife, as Sir Oliver had done. They appeared to speak and then they both came down the centre aisle together with their swords and rowels clanking at every step. At the main door they halted a moment and apparently spoke again, but whatever they said was inaudible. Then Sir Roger pulled open the heavy church door, and the two crusaders passed out into the night.

Gordon followed as closely as he dared with his movie-camera, and we all trailed after them right down the main road to Stalham, where they walked beside the Broad for quite a way.

The visit to the water's edge was marked by an ugly incident. From out of nowhere there suddenly sprang an eastern, evil-looking type of soldier, who flung himself upon Sir Roger with a fearsome-looking scimitar. I can hear the crash of that heavy steel sword as it cleaved its way through the knight's bevor, but like a cat his victim swung around and clutching him by the throat slowly closed his grip tighter and tighter till the Saracen just flung about like a serpent in his death struggle, lashing out with arms and legs, twisting and turning in its wild paroxysm of imminent dissolution. At last Sir Roger flung him into the reeds a dead man, and his inanimate body fell with a squelch into the soft mud in which the rushes were growing.

The two soldiers then re-traced their steps, back along the way they had come, and arriving at the church door, they passed in and knelt before the altar. They then returned to their respective resting-places and took up their original positions once more beside their still peacefully sleeping ladies. Then all was still once more, and the clouds continued their hurried journeys across the evening sky.

The following day we developed the plates, and on the one that we specially noted because of its being in the camera when the whole affair was knocked over, there was a cloudy 'extra' in the top left-hand corner, and in this vaporous emanation was the identical face that Gordon managed to get on his movie film, the face of Sir Oliver de Ingham, with a very thoughtful, sad, and pleading expression. The photographs generally were quite good. They showed the empty places when the knights had left their tombs, and the movie pictures turned out, considering all things, exceedingly well.

St Benet's Abbey

If I had only known then what I do now, wild horses would not have dragged me to this sacred spot on the evening of 25 May, and yet in our blissful ignorance we moored alongside the bank by the ruin, and imagined we had really struck an ideal spot. Had it been any other night but this one, I learned when it was too late, it would have actually surpassed our expectations, for it is really lovely there on any night except the one we hit upon.

For centuries and centuries, the slowly flowing Bure has glided past and laved the banks of this meadowland, which has more tragic history in its past than many better known places in the Kingdom.

In AD 690 a Christian hermitage was there, and when King Canute arrived in AD 1016, a monastery of the Black Friars or Benedictines had been long established there and was flourishing.

In those days land and property had to be safeguarded against attacks by invaders and maurauders, and so it came about St Benedict's Abbey-at-Holm, as it was always called, was not only a religious house, but a fortress as well, and all the inmates were trained like soldiers in the prowess of arms.

It can be easily appreciated how, on the arrival of an enemy, the monks would be called upon to defend their property and, promptly laying down their breviaries, pick up their swords, slings and crossbows.

And so it happened when in AD 1016 the Danish King Canute appeared on the horizon, all grazing cattle were herded inside the fortified walls of the Abbey, the big gates well-bolted and barred, and every man jack who could wield a weapon was called upon to do so. But the Danish King was not so easily to be withstood as the Abbot had imagined, and after laying siege to it for over two months, he put it to the torch and sent it up in flames. As soon as this had been accomplished, it must be said to his credit, he rebuilt it on an even more elaborate scale than ever, and the place has re-started under the same régime as before. The monks returned and the Abbot was pardoned for his resistance.

The religious at St Benet's carried on their work, and the Abbey became the great seat of learning for East Anglia, and by A D 1020 the senior house in the British province of the order. The remains of the Abbey that we see today with the brick tower of a mill erected in its midst is all that is left of Canute's handiwork. King Canute is interred in the sanctuary of Winchester Cathedral.

For many years unbroken peace reigned in the Abbey, and then the Conqueror came. St Benedict's withstood William of Normandy, and with the help of the surrounding peasantry put up a most stubborn resistance which lasted for nearly four months. The Duke's attacking forces were almost inclined to give it up and raise the siege, so impregnable did the monastery appear, but at last by a ruse they captured it. So well did the monks fight that it was only by a gross piece of treachery the Abbey fell. A soldier was sent across with a white flag and was admitted. Surreptitiously he slipped the janitor monk a note, asking his presence before the besieging general, who guaranteed him perfect safety.

When it came to a reply being sent back from the Abbey, he volunteered to take it, and, the permission being granted, he duly appeared alone before the general with his missive, in which surrender, conditional or otherwise, was refused.

The general then took the reverend brother aside and had a chat with him, and whilst the arms of the Abbey were fluttering defiantly in the breeze above the monastery walls, one of its inmates was treacherously selling his own brethren for a hundred shekels of silver.

'What are you?' enquired the general.

'I am a lay-brother,' replied Brother Veritas, for that was his name.

'Not even a priest, eh?' smiled the general.

'Alas no, sir.'

'Have to work pretty hard, eh?'

'Very hard, sir.'

'How would you like to be a priest, then?'

'Oh, sir. I'm not worthy enough.'

'Your humility fits you for even higher rank than priest. I have the disposal of the monastery in my hands, and can do what I like with it, but you can quite appreciate the fact that although an Abbot may have complete government and control within his monastery, yet he in turn has to be subject to the ruler of the Kingdom wherein his monastery is?'

'Yes,' meekly replied Brother Veritas.

'Now then, my friend,' went on the general, adopting a very definite and military attitude, 'if this Abbot of yours holds out over tomorrow, then I shall issue orders that every one within the monastery shall be put to the sword. If they open the gates tonight, as an act of submission, then they shall be spared, yourself included.'

The brother stiffened and went very pale, then blurted out:

'Oh dear, oh dear, that will never do. Supposing I opened the gates myself. I am the janitor.'

'Are you afraid of what the Abbot might do to you afterwards?'

'Yes,' replied Veritas, his voice trembling the same as his body at the thought of it. 'You see, I should be immured or something terrible like that for life.'

'Ah, yes, I see!' replied the general. 'Now we can easily overcome all that. We can take them all prisoners, depose the Abbot, anoint and ordain you a priest, and give you the Abbey on the spot. Then you would be perfectly safe. No one could touch you if you were the Abbot. You will not only be doing yourself a good turn, but you will be saving the lives of everybody in the monastery.'

'I'll do it!' exclaimed the lay-brother.

'Splendid!' barked the general. 'Tonight at sundown.'

'Tonight, at sundown. And you will keep your promise?' added the weakling.

'My promise? Take my sword and offer me the cross to kiss,' and handing his sword to Veritas, he kissed the hilt.

The brother was so impressed that he raced back to the monastery and told the Abbot that the general would put everyone to the sword if the monastery was not handed over by the following day.

'Never!' shouted the Abbot, in a terrific burst of rage. 'These thieving maniacs from Hell! Give up our monastery to them? Never! And he went purple in the face. 'The House of God to be given over to a horde of cut-throat barbarians? Not whilst I have a breath in my body.'

Then he summoned the Prior, the Reverend Precentor, Father Sacristan, and the Assistant Rector, and they all went into silent conclave in the chapel. They commended their souls to God, and decided unanimously to sit tight. They were perfectly safe, and no one could venture within the fortress, if they were strong enough to hold out as long as they had, they could still hold out, and would. There were sufficient supplies within the monastery to last them for twelve months, if need be, and they could afford to wait. A strict guard was kept at all points, and at night the sentries on the battlements were doubled.

The night following the promise of the general was very dark. Everywhere around was still, and although the air was soft and balmy, there was something sinister in it that made one draw closer inside their cloak, and give a little shiver. It was 25 May and spring had burgeoned in a wealth of flowers and lovely weather, and Brother Veritas was thanking his Creator for all the beautiful things in life and his ability to enjoy them, and was standing by the large heavy gate of the monastery peeping out through the grill into the tranquil night beyond, when a touch on his shoulder brought him to with a terrific start. Another brother had brought him a stoup of wine to cheer him up on his watch, and then went on his way singing in a blythe and happy voice one of the Psalms from the Vespers of that evening.

Veritas followed him with his eyes, and exclaimed: 'Ah, if he but knew!'

To him there was no qualm of conscience in what he had promised to do, for was he not going to save the entire monastery, and then, being made Abbot, he would be in a position to do so much more for his brethren than might ever come his way again. His hand itched for the bolts and the time appointed for the signal when he would undo the great door seemed never to come. He preened himself at the thought of his promotion and the exalted rank he would hold in the church, and there were one or two things he would have to say to the then Abbot, once he was deposed. His breast heaved with emotion at all these thoughts, and he could almost feel himself now a mitred Abbot, and experience a sense of great authority.

The big bell in the tower tolled the hour of eleven and its call resonated away over the marshes for miles, so deep, so full with it. The besieging troops heard it and gazed out into the darkness of the night from whence it came. Veritas's fingers were simply tingling with excitement awaiting the quarter after the hour, when he could expect the signal from the enemy without. The dripping of the water-clock was the only sound that broke the quiet and stillness near the gate. From his little room in the gatehouse he looked out upon the empty courtyard.

At last – yes, at last – the moment was at hand when from his menial and servile position he would be suddenly translated to the highest position of authority in the monastery. Three gentle taps repeated twice were audible on the great door, and Veritas stepped out to the portal. Three more taps from without, and his fingers nearly stiffened with anxiety. Then, taking his courage in his hands, he slid back the bolts gently and noiselessly, and lifting down the huge bar, the doors swung back on their hinges, and a body of men rushed headlong into the sacred fortress.

Brother Veritas was the first person to be seized and dragged away to the camp. Once the invading troops were inside, the place was theirs, for the resistance put up by the monks was as nothing.

Their main defence was gone, when the walls no longer kept the enemy without, and except for a few odd struggles the affair was over. The soldiery and the monks fraternised in good spirits, and arms were laid aside. But the following morning a great ceremony took place. The soldiers now held the keys of the friary, and into the great chapel filed the military, whilst the monks filled the gallery.

The general came in with a band of officers and stood in the choir. Then Brother Veritas was called, and to the intense surprise of all his brethren, he was brought before the altar, where he was anointed by a sergeant, a cope was placed around his shoulders, then the Abbot's mitre was placed on his head, and a crozier in his hand. In a loud voice the general then appointed him Abbot of St Benedict's-at-Holm for life. The real Abbot nearly fell back and collapsed in the gallery. Then, to everybody's surprise, the new mitred Abbot was bound with his hands behind him and dragged away by the soldiers to a gibbet. He shouted for mercy, but William's men had their own way of attending to these matters. Once outside, they placed a noose around his neck and hoisted him up in his full canonicals to a pole projecting from the lowest window in the bell tower, where everybody could see him. They had kept their promise, and then paid him in full for his treachery.

The general was so sympathetic towards the Abbot that their taking of the monastery was not allowed to inconvenience the monks at all.

The hauling up of the lay-brother by the neck, was a terrible punishment, and to see a richly vested being in cope and mitre kicking frantically in mid-air was and is still a sickening sight. I say 'still', because every year on the night of 25 May this same tragedy is enacted.

The mate and I were spreading ourselves on the deck on the evening in question two years ago, when suddenly the Abbey re-materialised itself out of its ruins; the mill tower which some clever person built within its sacred precincts in 1800, and which is familiar to all who know the place at all, vanished, and a magnificent stone church with a stone tower stood out against the midnight sky. In a few moments the entire monastery had taken shape again out of nothingness, and the whole place was suffused with a brilliant patch of local daylight. We were almost transported at the sight, and our pipes went out through sheer inattention, so absorbed were we by what we saw.

Then there was a terrific shemozzle, the gates were flung open, and a crowd of clamouring people poured out into the open. There were soldiers in armour and monks in their black habits swarming

163

and crowding with excitement. Then out of the chapel came a throng of soldiers and in their midst what appeared to be an Abbot in cope and mitre with his hands tied behind him. A rope was slipped over his head, and in a trice he had been hauled kicking, struggling and gurgling in mid-air.

No more nauseating scene can be imagined than this, and I have since made enquiries in many directions, but, as in relation to all other ghostly apparitions, you can get nothing out of the natives. Nevertheless, it is fairly well known by visitors, and I have had opportunities of comparing notes with several.

A party on the *Puffin I* in 1906 saw it, and as the owner is a near neighbour of mine, we have had good opportunities of discussing the vision. He also knows at least three different parties who have unwittingly found themselves present and witnessed this awful scene.

I advise all those who find themselves in that area on 25 May ever, to move on to some other place, where the berth alongside will not be spoiled by such a ghastly exposition as fell to our lot in the year of grace 1928.

Ranworth

In all East Anglia there is no place so associated with traditional history, legend and romance as centres around Ranworth, that most delectable and desirable of all the beauty spots that make the land of the Broads the most attractive holiday resort in all the Western Isles. From the main street of the glorious Bure it is not at first easy to find, for the entrance to its water-way is not very striking, being much like that of other spots of interest which border the sweetly flowing river. Often we come across a quiet, unimpressive little opening where the trees meet overhead and the banks are thickly lined with reeds, conveying nothing of any consequence beyond perhaps a pretty break in the river-side, where we can pull in and be so quiet that the rest of the world goes by and leaves you in an ecstasy of undisturbed tranquillity. The Broad-land is full of these, but when one puts the helm hard over and presses up the little side-water street o'erhung by willow and mountain ash, and that leads up to the Great Broad, one is filled with the same curious feeling one experiences on wending one's way up the carriage-drive to a large manor, which you are visiting perhaps for the first time.

At the inner end of the water-way you emerge into a large and beautiful mere. Facing you is the delicious little hamlet of Ranworth itself, which gives its name to the water, and to the right of it is the Hall, and still further to the right is the Old Hall, hidden by the timbered littoral of the nor'-west extremity of the Broad. On our port beam lie the famous marshes which extend to the Fleet Dyke and almost, if not quite, to the banks of South Walsham Broad.

Here we are in the Queen of the Broads, and around us Legend and Romance have drawn their mantles of tradition.

The atmosphere has completely changed, and the air seems charged with psychic forces which have come down through the ages, their imprints indelibly impressed upon our surroundings in a way which time will only serve to perpetuate. The luscious fragrance of the aromatic rushes which line the water's edge carry us back to the days when carpets were unknown and castle floors were strewn with them in their stead.

> Sabaean odours from the spicy shore
> Of Araby the blest.

It is like stepping back into the period when the Angevin monarchs held their sway, and England was indeed a Merrie England. (At least, we think it was.)

The very waters themselves of the Broad seem peopled with the Middle Ages, and at night they do say that, if one is very quiet, the monks of the monastery at Langley, many miles away on the river Yare, can still be heard chanting their Vespers from the depths of the placid waters beneath the boat.

From the priory in question there is, so tradition has it, a subterranean passage which leads to a large and magnificent chapel beneath the Ranworth Broad. Many people ask 'Why Langley?' thinking that the proximity of St Benet's-at-Holm would naturally have the greater claim, especially since Woodbastwick and South Walsham both came under its charge. As a matter of fact, Ranworth was given to the Abbot of Langley by Robert Fitz-Roger in AD 1195, and that was one hundred and eighty years subsequent to the foundation of St Benet's by Canute in AD 1020, but there was a church on this spot hundreds of years before St Benet's was ever dreamed of.

It is interesting to note that the Parish Church of Ranworth – the Cathedral of the Broads, as it is affectionately known today – stands as a permanent memorial to the first inception of Christianity in this country, for it was here in East Anglia that the closest association and trade was kept up between these Islands and the Continent in the early centuries, and there were over forty Christian Churches in the county of the North-folk alone when the Danes eventually ruled that part of Britain.

Nevertheless, it must be admitted that St Benet's did at one time have some small claims on Ranworth, if not very many, for we learn that the Abbot of St Benet's-at-Holm did release them in toto to the Abbot of Langley in AD 1285. But, it is additionally pleasing to note that the religious house at St Benet's did still retain an affectionate interest in the Parish Church of Ranworth, and were always ready with a helping hand if anything in the nature of repair or decoration was needed.

It is recorded that in AD 1538 they loaned the services of an exceptionally clever brother, one Pacificus, who restored and re-decorated what is without question today the most beautiful rood-screen in that part of England. For months and months he came daily to his great labour of love, accompanied by his little dog, who remained in the boat, and waited patiently for his master to row them home again at sun-down. And when he heard him coming he would hop out of the little boat and dance and bark with delight all around him. Across the Great Broad they'd go, the oars gently plashing their way through the white and yellow water-lilies that carpeted the surface of those quiet waters which led them to the Bure.

At early dawn, when Matins was over, that little craft, with little Caesar curled-up within, was already tied to the bank below Ranworth Church, and Pacificus had once more commenced his sacred task. When it was finished, and each carved rose spread out once more its gilded petals to welcome those who came to pray, Pacificus came no more. At least not for a while, for one summer evening, on returning to his abbey, he discovered it in flames, and on arrival found the place had been sacked and put to the torch. For years he lingered amidst the blackened ruins and eventually died there, but the local villagers who knew of his devotion to Ranworth took his body across the Bure and lovingly laid it to rest in the shadow of the church he had loved so well, and for which he had worked so hard.

And now he comes back to pray in the church where he spent so much time in his labour for God. Sometimes in the early hours of morning, when it is just light, his little boat is to be seen moored up to the bank, and a little dog asleep in it, waiting. Whenever that happens, the aged and saintly Benedictine is to be seen kneeling in an attitude of prayer before the centre opening of the rood-screen, and between the two parcloses. On the audible approach of anyone he is said to fade out into nothingness. Often has he been seen rowing his little boat home at nightfall with his little Caesar sitting up perkily in the stern.

It is on record that a learned divine, one James Brewster, D.D., of Baliol, on holiday at Horning last year (1930), was about to enter the narrow waterway up the Broad from the river, when he saw a weird-looking punt being rowed down it, and pulled into the side to make room. He waited and presently it passed. The rower was a monk in a black habit and had the kindest face he had ever seen in his life. The Benedictine smiled his thanks and passed out into the river where he immediately dissolved into oblivion. The reverend Dr Brewster thought there was a small white dog in the boat, but he

couldn't be sure. He was so moved by what he had seen that he made enquiries, but could learn nothing from the people at Ranworth, and at Horning he was laughed at.

That what he saw was our monastic friend, Brother Pacificus, going home after his labours there can be no question, and there is no real or known reason why it should not have been.

When Cavaliere Marconi has recovered the 'Sermon on the Mount' from the ether, and given the world a little more knowledge of undulations in the realm of space, we shall not be inclined to regard those things which to us today seem impossible, as fantastic figments of a disordered imagination. I often wonder what our grandparents would think of the Schneider Trophy Race or the lighting of a city with electricity in Australia by putting over a switch in Italy.

But Ranworth can also boast of another type of ghost, and this time it is connected with the Old Hall. Every year on the last day of December an awful apparition appears on the Broad, and has been seen so many times that familiarity has bred a contemptuous indifference to it locally, and it no longer begets fear in the native mind. The story, briefly is this:

Colonel the Hon. Thomas Sidney, who at one time resided at the Old Hall, was a high-stepper in his methods of life, and was noted far and wide as a convivial and bibulous roysterer. His wife was a charming, quiet, peace-loving creature who, in her frailty, suffered with passive resignation her fate when she allowed him to lead her to the altar, and accepted him for better or for worse. Their early married life was fairly happy, in spite of one or two punctuations, which she quietly forgave.

But she had reckoned without her host, and it was not until some years had elapsed and she had presented him with a son and heir, that she had awakened to the sad but incontrovertible conclusion that her husband was a monster and that she had tied herself for life to the crystalised climax of a long line of hereditary drunkards.

He would return from the chase sozzled and incapable, with his horse bleeding from deep spur wounds and nearly collapsing from hæmorrhage. He always boasted he could ride like the devil, and some went so far as to say that he *was* the devil. That he could outride most at the hunt was a fact, and many was the horse that fell dead under him as a result of his wild and inconsiderate contempt for its staying power.

Those who had seen him in the field galloping ahead of the others had often noticed a man in black on a large charger riding by his side, and when they had asked Thomas Sidney who he was, had been told to go to hell. The Colonel himself apparently had never seen him, or perhaps he might have mended his ways.

To torture a dumb animal always stimulated his appetite for blood-sport, and there was nothing he used to admit, that gave him so much pleasure after a long run as to come up with a panting fox that no longer had the strength to 'get away'.

The cruelties of the hunt he brought into his home, and many's the time a waiting-maid has taken the lash of his hunting whip which was intended for his delicate wife.

To drink himself under the table was a nightly occurrence, and, in his opinion, and I believe of most people of his day, this was a sign of honourable and noble birth. No gentleman ever went to bed sober. He was not only a 'three-bottler', but what we today would term a 'whole-hogger'. All night carousals were the joy of his brutal life, and his sexual appetite was a continual source of great anxiety to the families in the village who had female relatives employed at the manor.

It was not only in Ranworth that he was feared, for his lecherous proclivities carried his 'hunting' to many distant places, in one instance as far as Southwold. Distance was no object, and often the 'chase' lasted as long as a whole week.

He had no care or thought for God, man, or devil. He would hunt on a Sunday as readily as any day of the week, and on one occasion when the meet was held on Sunday morning outside the parish church, he cut the parson down with his hunting-crop for attempting to remonstrate with him and remind him it was the Sabbath.

This sort of thing, of course, was destined not to last, and his nemesis soon overtook him, which was only to be expected.

On the 31st day of December, in the year 1770, a great meet was held at the Old Hall, the greatest of the hunting season, and a hunt ball was arranged to follow in the evening.

During the halt for luncheon, which took place at the 'Rising Sun', at Coltishall, he made a drunken challenge to one of the riders that he would beat him in a ride to Hoveton-St John, which would be in the direction of their return home.

They started off, and the Colonel, infuriated with drink and contempt for his rival, was making a bad second, when suddenly he drew a pistol from his holster and shot the horse ahead of him. The animal stumbled and fell, badly throwing its rider. The Colonel rode on and arrived alone, to the plaudits of the rest of the hunt who had gone on before the race, in order to be present at the finish.

The hunt was continued, and after a hard day's riding, they returned to Ranworth Old Hall.

The unfortunate competitor in the race was thought to have given in, and gone back to his home at Belaugh, but truth to tell, he was found the following day by the side of his dead horse, with his neck broken.

The banquet that night was a great success, the Hall being crowded with the members of the hunt and the élite of the country-side. Over a hundred people sat down, and the tables groaned under their loads of luxury. The place was ablaze with light, and the wine flowed like water.

In the middle of dinner, just as the host had risen to his feet with glass in hand, and was about to propose the first toast of the evening, a footman touched him gently on the arm, and said:

'I beg pardon, sir, but there's a gentleman outside wishes to see you.'

'Tell him he can't!' snapped the Colonel. The footman went out, and returned just as the toast was being given.

'He says, sir, he must see you.'

'Oh, damn him, I won't see him. Tell him to go to hell!'

The servant withdrew and the glasses were raised in a shout of boisterous revelry.

Just as they had sat down, the doors opened, a tall, thin man in a close-fitting black robe rushed in, closed his skeleton fingers around the throat of Colonel Sidney, and dragging him forcibly out of his chair, lifted him up, kicking and shrieking, under his bony arm and raced out into the darkness with him, leaving behind a yellow smoke-screen of burning brimstone.

The assembly fell back choking and blinded, and fled to all parts of the house. The consternation was so great that women were thrown down and trampled on in the stampede to get away. People screamed, women were fainting, and the gentlemen, no longer the veneered members of a county aristocracy, cast their good breeding to the winds, and fought like tigers to get out.

Once outside, the chthonic intruder, with his kidnapped burden still yelling and shrieking alternately for help and then mercy, flung into the saddle of a seventeen-hands charger as black as himself, and rode hell-for-leather down the drive to the Broad, where he galloped across the mere, leaving in his wake clouds of steam which shot up with a loud hiss every time a hoof touched the water. Away into the darkness they rode, and Colonel the Hon. Thomas Sidney was never seen again.

And every night of 31 December since that eventful happening, that huge dark horse with red-hot hoofs and its rider bearing a struggling, shrieking man under his left arm, races out of the drive-gates of the Old Hall, and scatters the steam and spray in its mad career across the inky blackness of that peaceful mere.

If you have any reason to doubt it, turn up the *Transactions of the Metaphysical League*, Vol. XI, pages 173–219, and then, if your doubts are not set at rest, go down to Ranworth yourself, hire a boat, and moor off, under the pretext of a little fishing.

Wrap yourself up well, for it is bound to be a bit chilly, but nothing in comparison to the freezing of your liquor sanguinis when your Plutonic friend arrives with the man under his arm, who told him to go to from where he had just come.

So here's good luck to you, and before you attempt anything so hazardous, I ask you to put a codicil to your will and remember the Cathedral of the Broads.

If you don't catch many fish, your creel will return home with you replete to overflowing with experience and a firm determination never to laugh at a bigger fellow than yourself.

Bibliography

Notitia Dignitatum. (British Museum)

Domesday Book. (Record Office)

Anglo-Saxon Chronicle.

Land of the Broads (Suffling).

Charteres Pastoralum. (1533–1694 AD)

Gentleman's Gazette. (1607–1793 AD)

Country Pastorals (Wentworth).

The Saxon Shores (Mothersole).

History of England (Buckley).

Caerwithen Papers, Fol. XIII–XIX. (British Museum)

Memoirs of Lady Alys (Coverill).

Ranworth (Enraght).

Repertorium Ecclesiasticum (Oldfield).

Scripta Historica Islandorum.

Saga of Olaf Haraldsson.

Heima Kringla, or the Sagas of the Norse Kings.